ME AND THE SPITTER

Presented by

The Family of

Carl Barton

· · · · · · · · · · · · · · · · · · ·

Saturday Review Press/E.P. Dutton & Co., Inc.
New York

· · · · · · · · · · · · · · · · · · ·

ME AND THE SPITTER

An Autobiographical Confession

Gaylord Perry

With Bob Sudyk

*Published simultaneously in Canada by Clarke, Irwin & Company
Limited, Toronto and Vancouver*
ISBN: 0-8415-0299-4
Library of Congress Catalog Card Number: 74-245
Designed by The Etheredges

. . . .

*To my wife Blanche,
and my children
Amy, Beth, Allison and Jack*

. . . .

OFFICIAL BASEBALL RULES

8.02 The pitcher shall not—
   (a) (1) Bring his pitching hand in contact with his mouth or lips.

          PENALTY: For violating this part of this rule, the umpire shall warn the pitcher and if this action is repeated the umpire shall immediately disqualify the pitcher.

     (2) Apply a foreign substance of any kind to the ball;

     (3) expectorate on the ball, his pitching hand or his glove;

     (4) rub the ball on his glove, person or clothing;

     (5) deface the ball in any manner;

(6) deliver what is called the "shine" ball, "spit" ball, "mud" ball or "emery" ball. The pitcher, of course, is allowed to rub the ball between his bare hands.

PENALTY: For violation of any part of this rule (8.02 (a) (2 to 6)) the umpire shall:

(A) Call the pitch a ball, warn the pitcher and have announced on the public address system the reason for the action.

(B) In the case of a second offense by the same pitcher in the same game, the pitcher shall be disqualified from the game.

(C) If a play follows the violation called by the umpire, the manager of the offense may advise the plate umpire that he elects to accept the play. Such election shall be made immediately at the end of the play. However, if the batter reaches first base on a hit, an error, a base on balls, a hit batsman, or otherwise, and no other runner is put out before advancing at least one base, the play shall proceed without reference to the violation.

(D) Even though the offense elects to take the play, the violation shall still be recognized and the penalties in (A) and (B) will still be in effect.

(E) *The umpire shall be the sole judge on whether any portion of this rule has been violated.* (Italics Added)

ME AND THE SPITTER

1

The date was May 31, 1964—a day, I guess Billy Martin might say, that will live in infamy.

It was, almost any way you look at it, an historic day. I was with the San Francisco Giants, and we were playing the New York Mets at Shea Stadium, and a crowd of 57,037 turned out. The crowd set a record for the new stadium. What the crowd saw, the hardy ones that lasted it out, set a whole bunch of records:

1. They saw 32 innings of baseball—nine the first game, 23 the second—the most innings ever played by two major-league teams on one day.

2. They saw the longest doubleheader in history—nine hours and 52 minutes of playing time, almost ten and a half hours including the intermission. We started playing at one o'clock and just barely got to the showers by midnight.

3. They saw the longest game, in playing time, in history—seven hours and 23 minutes, breaking the old record by 23 minutes.

4. They saw the longest game, in innings, ever played to a decision in the National League. The only longer game up till then—a 26-inning affair—ended in a tie.

5. They saw 36 strike-outs in one game and 47 in the doubleheader—both major-league records.

6. They saw the Mets pull off the second triple play in their short history.

7. They saw Willie Mays play shortstop for the second, and last, time in his career.

8. And they saw Gaylord Perry throw a spitter under pressure for the first, but hardly the last, time in his career.

That final little item, I guess, took a long time to come to light.

On May 31, 1964, I became an outlaw in the strictest sense of the word—a man who lives outside the law, in this case the law of baseball.

On May 31, 1964, I started down—or up, depending on your point of view, I suppose—a path that would lead me through the mud ball, the emery ball, the K-Y ball, the Vaseline ball and the sweat ball, just to name a few. During the next eight years or so, I reckon I tried everything on the old apple but salt and pepper and chocolate sauce toppin'.

Of course, I'm reformed now. I'm a pure, law-abiding citizen. I've come to realize that spitting is a nasty habit, and unsanitary to boot. Unfortunately, a cloud of suspicion still hangs over my head, but that's not my fault. I can't help it if some people have suspicious natures, and most of them happen to be opposing managers.

I don't need to use that fancy stuff anymore.

But I sure needed it that day in Shea Stadium. I had to do whatever I could to get the Mets out. I knew I was taking a chance on getting kicked right out of baseball for throwing the spitter, but it was either that or wearing out the seat of my britches on the bullpen bench till it was time to hang up my spikes and head home to the tobacco fields of North Carolina.

And I wasn't ready to go home.

The doubleheader began peacefully enough. We won the first game 5–3. Orlando Cepeda stole home to give Juan Marichal the go-ahead run in the ninth inning. That was long before three knee operations were to turn Orlando into a limping designated hitter.

The second game looked like it was going to be even easier. We were ahead, 6–1, by the third inning. But the Mets, who didn't give anybody much trouble in those days, came back and tied the score, 6–6, in the seventh inning. Nobody dreamed then that it would be 16 innings later before anybody scored again.

Al Dark, our manager, waved me in from the bullpen in the bottom of the thirteenth inning. Frankly, there was nobody else left—except Bob Hendley, who was supposed to start the next day. And it wasn't just a case of saving the best for last. I was the eleventh man on an 11-man pitching staff. The twelfth man was in Tacoma.

The same time I came in, Dark made another strategic move. He shifted Mays, from his temporary spot at shortstop, back out to center field and switched Jim Davenport from third base over to shortstop. I guess Dark figured with me pitching, he had to bolster the defense any way he could. He turned out to be a genius.

I got in trouble right away in the thirteenth, and only a great throw from Jesus Alou in the outfield got me through.

We almost won the game in the next inning. Alou singled, Mays walked and Cepeda ripped a line drive over second base. Roy McMillan, the Met shortstop, was playing Orlando right up the middle. He caught the liner, stepped

13

on second and threw to first for a triple play. If that ball had gone through, I might never have started using the spitter. Then again, I suppose I might've.

By the time we got to the bottom of the fifteenth, there were about 10,000 diehards left in Shea Stadium. They were still blowing horns, clanking bells and having a good old time. There had already been at least ten fights in the stands.

Jim Hickman led off for the Mets in the fifteenth and singled off my fast ball. Charlie Smith dumped a sacrifice bunt at my feet, and Hickman took second. A couple of my infielders started to give me that fish-eyed don't-choke-you bum" look. I had to turn away from their stares.

Then my catcher, Tommy Haller, called time. He trotted out to me, very slowly, wearing that "we're-in-trouble" look on his face.

In the blue lights of Shea Stadium, I must have looked a little sickly. I sure felt a little sickly. Those lights turn your skin kind of greenish. I learned later that KSFO radio announcer, Russ Hodges, reported it to the folks back home in San Francisco: "Those bluish lights are something, fans. Gaylord looks like the grim undertaker out there on the mound."

Well, it sure looked like my funeral from where I was standing. Haller got to the mound and started telling me to relax and throw strikes. This is the kind of advice you always get when you're having trouble relaxing and throwing strikes.

"Gaylord," Haller said, "it's time to try it out."

We both knew what he was talking about, but I was surprised to hear Tommy say it. Haller had always insisted I didn't need the spitter. I used to argue that I did need it. Now he was trying to convince me I should use it.

"I dunno," I stammered. "I've never tried it with a game up for the takin'."

"Look. Alvin is staying with you, win or lose. We've been out here a long time today. I don't want to walk off

14

this field without all three of these games." Haller winked. That snapped the tension.

I knew what he meant. The second game was almost the length of two by then. We'd won the first one. Tommy already had been through 23 innings. In addition to being dead tired, he needed a shave.

"Gay," he said, "your stuff isn't sharp today. Let's give the Mets something new to look at. You'll never know for sure you can throw it until you try it when it counts. It's time to break the maiden, kid. I think you can do it."

My mind raced quickly. I had been working on the pitch for maybe a year. But the only times I used it in a ball game was when I had a big lead, which didn't happen too often back then. Sitting in the bullpen day after day, waiting for a chance to break into the rotation, I'd had a lot of time to think.

I was twenty-five years old, and I had spent most of my first six seasons in the minors. I had 55 victories and 46 losses in the bushes. The season before I'd gotten into 31 games with the Giants. I'd won one and lost six, my worst season playing any kind of baseball. And there I was on the mound at Shea on the last day of May with two wins and one defeat. I had made only seven appearances, all in relief. I hadn't started a game in a year. And I had an earned run average of 4.77, nothing to brag about.

I thought of my wife, Blanche, our very young children, and Mamma and Daddy back home on the farm. All counting on me. And me taking home only $9500 a year. I looked into the dugout at Dark. He hardly ever had anything to say to me. A manager driving for a pennant with a veteran pitching staff has little time for a struggling young pitcher. I couldn't blame him. On the staff were Marichal, Jack Sanford, Bob Hendley, Billy O'Dell, Don Larsen, Bob Shaw, Bob Bolin, Billy Pierce, Jim Duffalo, Ken MacKenzie—and me.

I remembered what veteran pitcher and good friend to

15

me, Bob Shaw, said out in the bullpen that day. Close as I can recall it, he said: "Gaylord, I don't think you've got enough right now to be a starting pitcher. There comes a time in a man's life when he must decide what's important. He must provide the best way he can for his family. You do that by winning in this game. That's the only thing that counts—winning. We're not high school boys anymore. Hitters are taking the bread out of your mouth. You have to learn all the tricks and then use them when you have to."

I had only a curve and a fast ball then. I was a power pitcher with *almost* enough power. I knew I needed something else, but I didn't know what—not until spring training of 1964. Then Bob Shaw joined the Giants. I noticed right away that some of his pitches traveled to the plate in a very unnatural way. My eyes near clean popped from my head. I knew how Tom Edison felt when he discovered the electric light. Bob Shaw promptly became my idol.

Shaw threw the illegal spitball, one of the best I've ever seen. Of course, he may deny it all now that he's been a pitching coach. Who can prove it, right? And let me say I'm positive Bob would never dream of teaching it to anyone he coached.

I figured if I could master that super pitch, I'd be buying time to develop some other pitches. Bob and I worked for hours. I studied his every movement. The old dew drop takes total dedication, like any new pitch you learn, only more so.

I had to learn how to load it up, how big a load the ball would carry, where to drop the load, how to grip the ball, how to release it, how to control it. And probably most important of all, how to hide it from four umpires, three coaches, a manager and 25 players on the field, as well as spying executives up in the box seats. Why, it was enough to give a poor country boy stage fright.

One time early in the 1964 season, I was so nervous, I loaded up one, and the ball dropped right out of my hand. And then I stumbled over it like a circus clown. Under

16

pressure, you can get pretty strange out on that mound. So I started spending hours in front of a mirror at home practicing my moves. Everything has to be natural and automatic. My wife wondered why I was spending so much time in front of a mirror. Well, I sure wasn't combing myself a new hairdo. Heck, I can comb my dome with a wet washrag in a dark closet, and Blanche knows it. But she never said a word.

Back there at Shea Stadium in 1964 I was worrying about being caught by the umpires, and about preparing the ball right. (Improperly loaded or thrown, the spitter will arrive at the plate and pause with "hit-me-here" written all over it.) I wasn't the most confident spitballer in the world. I couldn't have known then that in less than four years the Pittsburgh club would train four telescopic stop-action cameras on me trying unsuccessfully to detect my "wet wipe."

Haller kept looking at me. "Just concentrate on what you have to do," he said. "Use the decoy. Throw it when you can get it on the ball. Don't worry about me. You throw it. I'll catch it. Let's go."

By then, the Met fans were booing because of our conference. If they had only known what we were talking about. Poor plate umpire Ed Sudol seemed to be sagging right into the ground from the long day. I found out later that the umpires missed their between-game meal because the clubhouse boy was late.

I got the feeling a hungry umpire whose feet were barking would be in no mood for any shennanigans from a kid named Gaylord who was trying out a country boy's pitch in the big city. I couldn't be stalling on the mound. Fortunately, I was a kind of fidgety type on the mound anyway, skittering around like a fly dodging a horse's tail. The natural jitters helped me hide how I loaded her up. (Eventually I learned to go through decoys as though I was loading every time. That way, the batter never knew when it was coming. He'd start watching what I was doing instead of thinking about hitting the ball. Anyway, that's the strategy.)

Those days you were allowed by the rules to lick your fingers as long as you wiped them dry. A great decoy was going to the rosin bag after licking your first and second fingers. You bounced the dusty bag all around in your pitching hand. But those two fingers never got a touch of dry rosin. If you think that's an easy trick, try it sometime. I used to practice with my daughter's bean bag.

"Well, here we go," I said to myself.

Haller squatted down behind the plate. Hickman was on second and Chris Cannizzaro at bat. His weakness, according to my book on him, was hard stuff—sliders and fast balls. Haller didn't give me a sign. We both knew what was coming. I licked my fingers, faked a wipe and let her go as hard as I could, aiming for just above the knees.

She dipped into the dirt like a shot quail. Haller made a great body block, and Hickman held at second base. I was to need outstanding defensive help from everybody that day. The next pitch dipped about eight inches too low. Then Cannizzaro fouled my third super-sinker off the foot of umpire Sudol. He started hopping around. The crowd cheered.

I reloaded and fired off another spitter that was wide of the strike zone. Apparently, I overloaded. The ball came back from Haller still wet. Could I get one more pitch out of the same load? I thought why waste it? So I didn't decoy, and Cannizzaro figured he was getting a dry pitch. He missed it by a foot. I was learning already, and so was the Met manager, Casey Stengel. He was yelling "spitter" from the Mets' dugout, and Sudol was glaring at me.

I turned my back on home plate and faced my infielders. They weren't giving me that "he's-gonna-blow-the-game" look anymore. They guessed what I was doing and gave me that look of pride you get from your folks on graduation day.

Like any kid with a new toy, I was overdoing it. I had to put an awful lot on the ball to make it work then. I wasn't sure how big a load I needed. Too much was better than too little, I guessed. Meanwhile Stengel kept yelling to Sudol, "Call out the ground crew, Ed. Spread the rain tarp under him or this whole boomin' city might go under."

My next pitch to Cannizzaro was a hard fast ball up and in. He stopped his swing midway through the pitch. Sudol, probably happy not to get hit on the foot again, called ball four on a checked swing. Al Dark came charging out of the dugout. He really let Sudol have it. Then Sudol let Dark have it. He threw Dark out of the game for protesting a ball-strike call. Dark announced that he was playing the game under protest since his beef was over the checked-swing call and not the pitch.

The fans really cut loose. They were throwing everything on the field. When Dark returned to the dugout, he looked like a guy walking under an overturned garbage can. The umpires warned the fans to stop throwing debris on the field or the game could be forfeited to the Giants. On the air, Russ Hodges told his San Francisco listeners: "That reminds me of the time in Ebbets Field in Brooklyn in the late 1930s. Tex Rickert was on the public address system. Dodger fans were throwing things on the field. And one of the Cincinnati players was hit by a pickle. The umpires asked home-towner Rickert to warn the Dodger fans to stop throwing things at the Reds' players. Dutifully Rickert got on the P.A. and announced to the crowd, 'Don't throw no more pickles at the players!'"

Another fight broke out on top of the Mets' dugout. Everybody stopped to watch. Using the fight as a cover, I held the ball up to my mouth and spit right on her just like I read Burleigh Grimes used to do. Nobody saw me do it, especially Cannizzaro who was on first, Hickman

19

on second and Galen Cisco, the Met pitcher, in the batter's box. Cisco didn't have a chance. He bounced the first pitch right back to me. The son-of-a-gun was still loaded. It slipped from my grip when I threw it to Jimmy Davenport covering second base. He made a great leaping catch and came down on the bag. He leaped again to avoid the runner and threw to Cepeda at first, who dug it out of the dirt for a double play. We were out of the inning. Cepeda rolled the ball along the grass, tumble-drying it by the time it reached the mound. Everybody protects a spitball pitcher.

When I got to the dugout, Bob Shaw was grinning. He slapped me on the back. Later, he said something like "Nice going kid, you made it." Shaw may claim loss of memory. He'll deny helping me learn the "super-sinker." I will not challenge him on it. This is part of the brotherhood, never to challenge a member of the clan. Right, Bob?

Haller was laughing. "Reduce the load of juice, Gaylord," he said. "Sudol's getting suspicious of that splashing sound in my mitt."

By the sixteenth inning, everybody was hungry and beat out. It reminded me of a dawn-to-dark day pulling tobacco down on the farm. I had pitched two innings the day before. I was a little shook by everything, too. At bat in the nineteenth inning, I took two pitches before umpire Sudol called time. He noticed I'd forgotten to wear my batting helmet. I was an easy out, but I was hoping Mays would bust one to end it. Willie had only one hit in ten trips in that second game. Willie later admitted using a lighter and lighter bat each time up till it looked like a Little League model.

When he came to the plate in the nineteenth, Sudol said, "That bat's illegal."

Mays replied, "Then kick me out."

Sudol said, "If I'd known we'd all be out here this long, I wouldn't have kicked Dark out!"

And I wasn't out of the woods, either. In the nine-

20

teenth, I couldn't get the right amount of moisture on the ball when I needed it. My mouth was on the dry side and the more I got concerned about it, the drier it got. On top of this, I was tiring. When I stepped out of the dugout to face inning 20, I saw doom.

"Hey, Gaylord, wait a minute," called a veteran pitcher whose name I seem to have forgotten. "Here's something for your sore throat."

"I ain't got a sore throat," I replied.

"Sure you do, kid. Open wide." I opened, and into my mouth popped a round, brownish tablet. It was about the size of a dime. It didn't taste like anything.

"Suck on it awhile. Then go to work. It'll last you about three innings. If Sudol comes out to look, just swallow it. It won't hurt you none, kid."

That was my first taste of slippery elm. My mouth was watering like a hungry hound's at eatin' time. Suddenly I felt like a pitcher again. With the mouth-watering elm, my confidence came back. If I'm going to pitch it, I might as well use what it takes to load it up right. It was a breeze from then on. I gave up a couple of singles to Frank Thomas and Charlie Smith. But I struck out four Mets in the final three innings I worked.

In the top of inning 23, the Shea organist was playing "We Just Couldn't Say Good-bye" followed by "Rock-a-bye Baby," and a couple of guys jumped on top of the dugout and danced a waltz together. What a day! I'd pitched ten shutout innings. Finally, with two out, we got to Galen Cisco, who himself had pitched eight shutout innings. Jimmy Davenport drove a liner into the right-field corner for a triple. Cap Peterson was intentionally walked. Del Crandall, the fortieth player in the game, was called in from the bullpen to pinch-hit for me. He rifled a ground-rule double, scoring Davenport. Jesus Alou beat out a roller, and Peterson scored. Then Bob Hendley came in and wrapped it up for me in the bottom of the twenty-third.

We had finally won, 8–6. I had my third victory of the season, the first spitball victory of my career.

As I stood wearily under the relaxing force of the hot spray of the showers that midnight, my mind drifted back to my youth to another shower bath at Williamston High in North Carolina. I was fifteen years old and never had known what a shower bath was until my freshman year. And Williamston High housed the first indoor toilet I had ever known.

I thought, too, about the spitter I had thrown that day, and Al Dark's handshake after the game that was to make me a regular starting pitcher from then on. I thought about becoming an outlaw pitcher—according to the rules of the game, but not according to those who play the game. The spitter was to make me a winning pitcher until I could develop the pitches I needed on the dry side of pitching.

I'm glad now that I never stopped working on the dry pitches. The spitter rule was changed before the 1968 season, and again before the 1974 season, and each change made it a little more difficult for a man to earn a living wetting up a baseball.

I'm glad, too, that I did learn how to throw the spitter—and later the greaser—even though I've given up those black arts. Of course, a lot of people say I haven't given up those pitches, and some people—including a few umpires—say I *never* threw those pitches.

I'm not going to call either side liars. A pitcher who does not throw a spitter or greaser, but has batters believing he does, has a phantom pitch and an advantage. A pitcher who can slick one up effectively has twice the advantage. Do I still wet them? I sure know how. But that doesn't mean I do it—or even that I ever did it. Maybe I'm just kidding. Maybe I got the Mets out in 1964 on sheer talent.

. . . .

2

. . . . . .

"C'mon, Gaylord, tell me, where do you get it?"

That's been *the* question going on ten years now. It's usually followed by a snicker and a couple of light jabs to my ribs. It's like people dying to know how a magician does his card tricks. Everybody always wants to know how I load up my wet one—and I mean *everybody*.

During a reception in the White House before the 1970 All-Star game in Washington, Commissioner Bowie Kuhn introduced the players, one by one, to Richard Nixon. When he got to me, the President gave me one of those Paul Bunyon handshakes that win elections. Then he lightly jabbed his elbow in my ribs and whispered, "Gaylord, tell me, where do you get it?"

I thought, "Not *you* too?" "Mr. President," I said,

"there are some things you just can't tell the people for their own good."

He roared and said, "You'd make as good a politician as you are a pitcher."

Another time, back home during Christmas holidays, I played Santa Claus for a bunch of youngsters. I had the red suit on, the beard and all the stuffing to make me round. All in all, I thought I was pretty well disguised. There was a string of kids waiting to talk to me. I was pulling each one up on my knee and asking what he wanted Santa to bring him for Christmas. Then one kid hopped up and asked, "Gaylord, do you throw a spitball?"

Why, even a messenger of the Lord once knocked on my door and popped *the* question. Rev. George Plagenz, who doubles as religion editor of the Cleveland *Press*, stopped by my Cleveland apartment during the 1972 season.

"Gaylord," he said, "I know you wouldn't tell a lie to a preacher. Tell my congregation you don't throw the spitter, and they'll believe you."

Wow. I told him, "I wouldn't lie to you, Reverend. I'd certainly like to answer your question, but that would spoil the whole idea. And I know you wouldn't want to do that."

My good friend and favorite detective, Billy Martin, brought The Great Search to its most sophisticated level in 1972. Billy, then managing the Detroit Tigers, has a pretty good-sized nose on his head to snoop with. It was in September, about the fifth inning of a duel between me and Woody Fryman. The Tigers were going for the division championship. We were just going for the end of the season. Billy called time and walked out to plate umpire Bill Kunkle.

"I can prove he's putting something on the ball," Martin said.

"Look, Billy, I've checked the ball a dozen times

already. I've inspected him. I can't find nothing." Kunkle removed his mask.

"I know, I know," Martin said. "But I want you to do something that will prove he's putting something on the ball."

"What?"

"Smell it. Go on, smell it!"

Kunkle held the ball under his nose, sniffed it, looked at Martin and shrugged.

"Well, do you smell it?" Martin snapped.

"Hell, I can't smell nothing," said Kunkle. "I got an awful stuffed-up head cold."

It's been going on like that for years now. At the suggestion of umpires, usually inspired by a manager, I've had to take off my pants, my shirt, one shoe and even my cap, which is embarrassing, because I ain't got much hair on my head. I've had to towel-dry my face, neck and arms before as many as 50,000 fans. I've given my glove to umpires who have done everything but turn it inside out. And, I've been the selected short subject of stop-action movies in two cities and the target of still photographers hired by ball clubs in other cities.

They were all after one thing: to find out where I kept whatever I was supposed to use on the ball. There was a time when those suspicions certainly had a basis in fact. But that was before I reformed, before I said goodbye to slippery elm, Vaseline, K-Y Jelly, baby oil, scuffballs— anything that would help me get out a batter.

Of course, even though I'm out of the funny business, I could still teach the art of loading 'em up. It's like learning to ride a bicycle or to roller skate—once you know how you never forget.

When I came up to the big leagues in 1962, under the existing rules, spitballing was not complicated. Making the spitter behave was another thing, but loading it up was

25

easy. Some pitchers were really careless. We true masters had little respect for them. Slobberers, we called them. Those clumsy, over-enthusiastic spitballers not only showed no respect for a delicate art, they actually triggered the rule change in 1968 that ended finger-licking on the mound.

Before the new rule, the simplest form of loading the ball was merely wetting the first two fingers of the pitching hand, then faking a wipe-off. Anybody could do that, even a farm boy from North Carolina. Or you could walk off the mound and spit on your hands while you were rubbing up the ball. You practiced that enough and you could keep those two key fingers wet while still wiping the ball up hard. Like the carnival pitchman says, "The hand is quicker than the eye." They tell me Lew Burdette of the Braves used to spit between his teeth to load his fingers. I couldn't master that. I read where Preacher Roe of the Dodgers used to spit in the palm of his hand while reaching up to wipe the sweat off his brow. He could hit it on the move. Then he'd pick up the spit with the two business fingers.

My own favorite method was wetting up the back of my thumbnail area at the same time I was wetting my first two fingers with a natural and legal lick. It was undetectable by the human eye. And even by the camera eye, I might add. Then I'd wipe the two fingers dry, just in case anyone was watching. But while I was getting my sign from the catcher, I'd flick those fingers over the back of my thumb and get the ball ready for my super pitch. No one knew when I had it, not even my catcher. I always had a few special signs to let him know I was loaded up.

Just to review the process, nice and slow: first, I wet up the back of my thumb (it could stay wet for three or four pitches) while licking my first two fingers. Then I wiped real hard two or three times with my first two fingers pressed against my uniform. I wanted to make sure the batter and the bench saw me drying off. But I kept the wet backside of my thumb, by the nail, facing away from my shirt. Next I flicked my first two fingers over the thumb to get the moisture. And then I just threw my super-sinker, aiming right above the knees. Get it? The umpires never did.

The next pitch, I'd lick my fingers again. But then I'd execute a casual wipe-off that looked like a fake to the batter and his coach. They thought, "Well, here she comes again." But I wouldn't load it off my thumb that time and, instead, I'd throw a fast ball. By then, the hitter would get a little confused. He'd be wondering, "Well, is he or isn't he wetting them up?"

Then I'd work him with a couple of curves. He'd be looking for the sinker both times. Next pitch, with only a flick of my first and second fingers, I'd get the saliva off my thumb again while getting a sign from my catcher. All the while, the batter would be watching me. He'd see that at no time during those last two pitches did I go to my mouth or even blow on my hands. He'd feel confident I wasn't coming in with my sinker. He'd be looking for a breaking ball, and, naturally, I'd let him have one of my loaded-up sinkers.

In all honesty, I didn't wet it up nearly as often as a lot of pitchers in the game. But one thing that put me ahead of most of the other guys was that I was never afraid to use my dew drop in a crucial situation, when I needed a big out. I favored the spitter in those situations while other pitchers got a little cautious. A teammate of mine in San Francisco, Ronnie Herbel, had a great wet one, but he was afraid to use it in tight spots. I think it bothered him a little to twist the rules.

The reason I didn't have to use the super-sinker too often was that I worked so hard on developing my decoy —a series of motions designed to make the batter think you're throwing a spitter even when you're not. (In a sense, I've got to admit, this book isn't a bad decoy, either.) I'm not kidding when I say that the effectiveness of the super drop depends on the decoy as much as on the pitch itself. You have to get the batter watching your decoy—and then to know when to use the real thing.

One of the big problems with the 1974 rule change—it's in italics right at the front of this book—is that the spitter or greaser call is now a judgment call. The umpire doesn't need any evidence, just an opinion. Which means I'm going to have to cut out my decoying, or at least cut down on it, for fear I'll be faking out the wrong people—the umpires. Otherwise, they might convict an innocent man.

Every wet-ball pitcher develops his own decoys. I wanted to keep things simple. Just a tug at my cap gave me an easy decoy. I'd go to my mouth, touch my cap and deliver the ball. Actually I had to tug at my cap anyway; I was balding and I had to keep pulling at it to keep it on my head in the Candlestick Park wind tunnel. It wasn't long before some of the hitters began to figure there was some connection between my spitter and the way I tugged at my cap. That was jim-dandy with me. I used it as a decoy and kept it when I switched from spit over to Vaseline.

Hank Aaron, for one, used to really get bugged by my decoying. Once, late in the 1967 season, we were playing Atlanta. I'd get my sign, give my cap a tug and Hank would back out of the batter's box. Then he'd step in and give me a disgusted look. I'd get the sign again, tug again and Hank would step out. This happened twice more. Finally, he stepped out and yelled, "Throw that blankety-blank and I'll take it outta here."

So I tossed up a big, old, slow roundhouse curve. Hank was so geared up to go downtown with one of my sinkers that he couldn't unwind himself in time to do anything. The pitch floated lazily right through the heart of the strike zone. Hank looked down at the plate and splashed it with a wad of spit that would have lasted me three innings. He turned to umpire Doug Harvey. "Why

don't you just let him carry a bucket of water out there?"
Henry said. I was hurt; that pitch was as dry as a Baptist
wedding.

But Mr. Aaron has got the best of me a couple of times
over the years. I gave up his six hundredth homer, and he
beat me with another homer in the 1972 All-Star game.
Those are the only two he got off me. I'll tell you, one of
the bonuses of being traded to the American League was
that I wouldn't be the guy who served Hank the homer
that broke Babe Ruth's record.

Besides keeping the batters guessing, I knew I had
to decoy the first- and third-base coaches. They'd watch me
to see if my fingers got wiped dry on my uniform. So I'd
move around a lot on the mound. I'd turn my back to the
coach at first. That'd take care of him. And I'd face the
third-base coach squarely, which made it difficult for him
to see if I was wiping. My shoulder blocked off the batter.

Sometimes I'd let the coaches see an obviously fake
wipe. They'd tip off the hitter that I was loaded up. And
then I'd throw a breaking pitch. Sometimes it was funny
to see the batter going one way and the ball the other.
Funny for me, not the batter. I'd try to cross the coaches
up right at the start of the game. A batter who loses confidence in his coaches' signs will ignore them the rest of
that game.

The Giants, including me, tried hard to figure out Don
Drysdale of the Dodgers. Everybody thought he got his
moisture from his belt. Then he'd rub his thumb and first
finger, as if he was really rolling up something slick. Like
he had it good. Then he'd go to his pants and wipe his
thumb hard on his leg. We tried to guess his spitter that
way, but we missed so many times. Dick Dietz, once
looking for a sinker, nearly had his head taken off with a
hard fast ball high and inside. It only took one pitch like
that from Don, and Dietz didn't want to guess any more.

There were no pre-game preparations necessary when
practicing the art of the spitball. All you needed for a game

was about three slippery elm tablets to suck on, two damp fingers, the skill of an actor and the guts of a burglar. But in 1968, the new rule complicated the art.

It was during the winter before the '68 season that the rules committee decided a pitcher would no longer be allowed to touch his fingers to his mouth as long as he was anywhere near the mound. Wetting up the fingers was outlawed for all practical purposes. The spitball era was over. Today, people still talk about the spitter, but the spitter is dead. Nowadays, it's a grease ball the pitchers are throwing. The new rules ended some careers and caused others to decline, for logical reasons. Some of the spitballers couldn't adjust to the use of Vaseline, K-Y jelly, oily hair tonics and other slicky products. Actually, the rule change was a hardship on law-abiding pitchers, too—the ones who learned to pitch wetting their fingers, then truly drying them before every pitch.

I had to switch to a lubricant and learn how to apply it and hide it. Then I had to show each team I faced in 1968 that I could still get what I needed when I needed it. Once I established myself against a lead-off batter, I might never need to throw the greaser again for the rest of the game. But they'd all be watching for it. That year, I guess some of us proved that oil and water can mix.

The first time I faced the Cincinnati Reds in 1968— early May, as I recall—Pete Rose led off the bottom of the first inning. A perfect test case. I wound up and gave Charlie Hustle my slick one on the first pitch. He missed it by a foot.

"Well," he yelled, sarcastically. "It's good to see you haven't changed!"

Pete must not have been in a good mood that day because he started yapping at the plate umpire. The two of them got into it. Then I went through the usual decoy three straight times and threw Rose three straight change-ups to strike him out. He was so mad he started arguing the whereabouts of the strike zone and the umpire threw him out of the game.

Rose turned to me and yelled, "Hey, Perry, where do you keep your dip stick?"

"What do ya mean?" I said.

"How else will you know when your cap needs an oil change?"

Rose used to get real hot at me, just like Aaron. Bobby Murcer and Mike Epstein are a couple of American Leaguers who aren't too fond of me—professionally, that is.

The Giants had gotten advance word on the new rule at the end of the 1967 season. So I started nosing around that winter. Through the grapevine, I found out what I had to do: first, I had to get my arm stronger. The super-sinker is a tough pitch on the arm because of the way the ball is released. With all the experimenting ahead, I knew I'd need to be in top condition. Second, a more complicated set of decoys would be needed. I decided on six: hand to the hat, hair, ear, neck, wrist, to some part of my uniform before delivery—all automatically without having to think. In the early spring training games of '68, I went through all those motions without ever trying to load up a ball. The clubs out in Arizona must have thought I had the St. Vitus Dance.

The Giants' front office didn't say anything to me. But I knew manager Herman Franks and general manager Chub Feeney were wondering what I was going to throw up there. I could tell from the looks they gave me that they were a little concerned.

I finally caught onto the grease pitch after weeks of experimenting. Ironically, it was in a spring training game against Cleveland that I finally got her working. It was pretty much the same technique as the spitter, but without spit.

After that game, manager Franks came over and slapped me on the back. "Kid," he said, "that super-slider of yours has finally come around. It looks simply great!"

31

I got the message. We were going to call my greaser a slider. That way, management and me would know what we were talking about when it came up in conversation. If somebody came up with charges or writers asked questions we didn't want to hear, we, at least, would be talking the same language. But right here I'm gonna call my greaser just what it was, a greaser, so as not to confuse anybody any more than necessary.

The first couple of years, I had to use gobs of stuff. I put it on my cap, my pants, my shirt, underneath the tongue of my shoe and on my belt. As the umpires started checking me more and more, I realized I was only safe applying the lubricants to exposed skin, like my neck, forehead, wrist, ear and my hair. I'd always have it in at least two places, in case the umpires would ask me to wipe off one. I never wanted to be caught out there without anything. It wouldn't be professional.

Lubricants were hard to detect. Like, you'd have some on your forehead. As you'd sweat, it'd all blend together. And no matter where you had it hid, you got a lot of time to clean off before any umpire could get out there to inspect you. The manager would come out and argue with the ump. That'd take 15 seconds. Then the two of them'd walk some 60 feet to the mound. Heck, in a few seconds, I could make myself legal. You never put it all over you. Otherwise, you'd look like you had the mad itch trying to wipe off a dozen places before the ump got to you.

Just like with the spitter, I quickly got to where I needed less and less grease to do the job right. Vaseline proved to be the best lubricant. As I became expert, I only had to rub a thin coating over my face and neck. It was like an actor's greasepaint make-up, and after all, wasn't I a kind of actor out there? The lubricants were blending right in with my sweat, making nothing detectable, and together, the two were more slick than spit.

Decoying the greaser was pretty much the same as decoying the spitter. I'd load up from, say, my neck. Then

I'd go to my cap, forehead, cheek, hair and ear, all real quick. Then I'd throw the super-sinker. The next time I wouldn't touch anything, but I'd have loaded up enough for two. I'd come back with another greaser. Then I'd go to my cap maybe two, three times, making sure the batter noticed me. He'd be looking for another greaser, and I'd give him a curve or a changeup. Soon as he got feeling puzzled, I felt good.

Of course, the pitch wasn't fool-proof. I once threw Willie Stargell a truly outstanding super-sinker, and he hit it a truly outstanding distance. He was looking for it all the way, and I watched it go all the way—about 455 feet.

Unlike the spitter, the greaser requires some pre-game prepping. I'd start out with a thin coat of lubricant on my forehead when warming up. I always believed in simulating game conditions when warming up. By game time, I'd have to grease up again in the dugout. Depending on the weather, the game situation and whether I was using K-Y or Vaseline or something exotic, I had to replenish my grease supply four, five or six times a game. I preferred to grease up in the runway, out of sight. But sometimes I had to do it on the bench, in front of my teammates. Then I tried to be a little tricky about it, make it obvious I was putting it in one spot and try to sneak it onto a second spot, too. I didn't want them to know too much. Why? Because guys do get traded. Some of them, I knew, would wind up playing against me. Some used to watch me like a hawk.

I don't want to give the impression that my teammates were against me. Besides the help I got from their bats and gloves, they'd sometimes give me grease checks. Once, Jimmy Davenport looked me over like a top sergeant in an Army field inspection.

"Atten-tion!" he yelled.

I came up straight off the bench. He strutted around me checking my uniform, my glove and then me.

"Gaylord, this is a disgrace. You got it a little too

heavy right here on your neck. Why, I can see my reflection on your forehead."

I wiped some off and asked, "Sir? How is it now?"

"Hmmmmm. Better. You got to be more careful, young man."

"Am I ready?"

"You look like you can do it now," he replied with a straight face. The other guys were cracking up.

Once, during an important game against the Dodgers, my second baseman, Hal Lanier, called time and trotted over to me. "Gaylord, will you please cut down on the load? We're throwing sinkers all over the infield now. If you keep putting that much on it, I'm gonna have a better one throwing to first base than you got throwing to the plate."

Because batters tend to hit sinking pitches into the ground, I always needed a good defensive infield. Orlando Cepeda and Willie McCovey, Jose Pagan, Lanier, Davenport, Tito Fuentes and later Chris Speier helped make me a 20-game winner in San Francisco. They and my catcher tried to help me load the greaser, too. But it didn't work out. They'd put it in the wrong place on the ball, or it'd get smeared off in the gloves.

From time to time, I used to notice my locker being burglarized. You know, I'd find my stuff moved around. You got to expect thieving, especially on the road. I heard about opposing players sneaking into my locker and looking into my pockets to see what I had. But I was up to 'em. Sometimes I still leave a little bait out. A tube of graphite, a can of sewing machine oil, a bar of Ivory soap or maybe a little cooking grease. It's fun to walk out to the mound to pitch and see them smirkin' in the dugout like they know something. Heck, I got to have a little fun, too. I'm always telling the trainer to leave some K-Y jelly lying around the training room, hopin' somebody'll see it and spread the word. Anything to get them thinking about my super pitch.

The reason a lot of pitchers don't throw the greaser has nothing to do with ethics. They just can't master it. For those who can, it means victories, big money and a longer career. But it's very difficult to throw the greaser consistently well. It takes a very delicate feel to release a ball barely held with slick fingers.

Normally, the baseball is gripped with the first two fingers over the top and the thumb underneath. The fingers make the last contact with the ball when it is released. The normal spin is backspin, or toward the pitcher.

But the spitter or greaser rolls in a forward rotation, toward the batter. It is released with hard pressure by the *thumb,* the slick fingers on top hardly making contact with the ball. The thumb is the last contact with the ball as it is released. I've read it described as the same action as squirting a wet watermelon seed from your fingers. It is a tricky pitch. The slick load must be in the correct place, the finger release just right, the arm motion perfectly coordinated for the pitch to sink and be controlled. It takes a long time to master. I can make that pitch break in, out, up or down. And I learned that the farther toward the end of my fingers that I held the ball, the heavier it would arrive at the plate and the more it would sink.

When I started throwing it, I didn't know exactly how much stickum to apply. When you use too much, the ball floats to the plate like a knuckle ball. It can be spotted by a batter in time for him to adjust to it. When you learn to get the same action on the ball using less spit or grease, the ball rotates more and looks like a fork ball. There are no two spitballers exactly alike. Some exert tremendous squeezing force when they throw it. Mine is a kind of snap, like the jaws on a crocodile snatching at something. (No two spitballs are exactly alike, so I don't know how any umpire can spot one for sure with the naked eye, as the 1974 rule change demands.)

How many I threw in a game varied with the closeness of the game and the sharpness of my other pitches. I've gone through some games without throwing one, and others throwing sinkers 90 percent of the time. It never mattered how many times I threw it so long as the batters thought they saw it on every pitch. I never got callouses on my thumb or my fingers from throwing it, but in the beginning, there were times my fingers grew tired before my arm did.

Here is what actually happens to the ball when you release it. It rotates forward slowly. When a ball travels through the air (like a knuckle ball) in a slow, angled rotation, the airflow causes it to blow off course or break. And because gravity is involved, any downward rotation is intensified. You see, the lubricant on my fingers lessens the friction at the point of release and reduces spin on the ball. Some think that the amount of slickum on the ball deflects the airflow and makes the pitch break. But some scientist checked it out and found that to do that, a pitcher would need a layer of grease about the height of the stitches on the ball. In the first place, the umps would notice a load like that. And the action of the ball would not be affected unless, of course, you had the right release. It's the reduced friction that counts—not the added substance. A lot of people in the game who know nothing about the pitch have tried to trap me. Whitey Herzog, the Texas manager, tried to pull something on me in the 1973 season. In the seventh inning of a game, he came charging out of the dugout with a ball he said I used in the game. Some of my writer friends saw the illegal object after the game. They told me it had a covering of grease the size of a half dollar. There's no way I'd ever do that. It was a phony all the way, but it made for a great rhubarb. Whitey got thrown out of the game.

My catcher was always very important in keeping my greaser secret. I had one spot on the ball where I loaded up every time. He'd know the spot. (Billy Martin says I keep messing up the league president's signature with my slickum.) Often the ball would dry on the way to the plate. If it didn't, it would get wiped off in the pocket of the catcher's mitt. If the umpire wanted to check the ball, the catcher gave it a quick smear with his thumb to clean off the spot while handing it to the ump. And the umpire himself unconsciously would provide the final wipe, just handling the ball to look for a foreign substance. I needed so little grease toward the end of my grease-ball career that it was undetectable. In fact, there is no way umpires or batters can prove I haven't been fictionalizing my spitter and greaser in this book. They have never found a thing on the ball. And they never will. They've never thrown me out of a game while pitching, and they've never found anything on me.

Why am I telling all this now? Because I feel the spitter—the greaser—has been good to me, and I want to be good to it. I think the spitter has added controversy and excitement. It has livened up more ball games than wearing doubleknit uniforms and letting hair and whiskers grow. With all the controversy surrounding me and the spitter, I thought baseball fans might like to know the truth. It's right smarter, in my opinion, for everyone to know about the pitch instead of just condemning it. Maybe it'll help folks understand why many players and managers believe the slippery pitch should be legalized. And why they don't blame a pitcher who can get away with it.

Hopefully, the rules committee will lean a little more toward allowing the pitch again after reading the first book on it. The rules committee in December, 1973, gave the umpires more power to call spitters or greasers on their own judgment. Seems to me that the umpires have enough to worry about without placing that extra burden on them. If the pitch was legal, they'd have no problems. And maybe neither would I.

I'm still hoping the slippery pitch'll get the Good Housekeeping seal, and then I can go back to using it again. I know I'm not ashamed of having used it in the past. After all, I was following in some pretty distinguished footsteps. As for the ethics, well, the main ethic of baseball is simple: win. I can't see what's wrong with throwing a pitch few other people can master that helped me win.

What do I do these days to win ball games?

Well, let me tell you where I hide what goes on my pitches now: why, in every pore of my body. It's plain, natural, body-produced sweat. Sometimes, accidentally, it may even get on the ball. And it doesn't hurt any that the Good Lord has blessed me with oily skin. They can't put a rule in the books against you sweating. That'd be un-natural. And if just enough sweat gets on my finger so that I could turn a page of this book, why that'd be enough for the ball to act a little strange. It took me ten years of big-league pitching to reach this point of refinement.

Oh, there's one other thing. My last year with the Giants, I began working on a fork ball. It's not a ball you throw with a fork. All you do is split wide your first and second fingers and hold the ball between them. You throw it hard, but it goes up to the plate easylike, then sinks. A lot of batters mistake that for a slicky pitch.

There's no question about it: I couldn't have won the Cy Young Award in 1972 if I hadn't learned the fork ball.

3

Even though I never owned up publicly to throwing a spitter or greaser, not till the day I sat down to work on this book, I guess my little secret has gotten around in recent years.

The Boston *Globe*, which is supposed to be a respectable newspaper, was real tough on me in 1973. They flatout said I was a criminal. They pronounced me guilty until proven innocent.

First, they quoted Bob Bolin of the Red Sox, a former teammate and friend of mine, as saying, "Gaylord Perry has been approached by every investment firm in San Francisco. After all, he's the man who took a 39-cent jar of vaseline and made himself a $100,000 pitcher."

And if that wasn't enough, Bill Liston of the *Herald-*

Examiner wrote, "Spitballer Gaylord Perry will face the Sox tomorrow. . ."

He tried me and convicted me, just like that. The Boston papers give bank robbers and mass murderers more benefit of the doubt than they gave me.

One time, a lawyer came around and asked me whether I might be interested in launching some legal action against the players and the reporters who called me a spitballer. "Gaylord," the lawyer advised me, "if they can't prove you're throwing a spitter, you've got a helluva case. You can sue all of them for defamation of character. You can even project a loss of income."

"How much money could I get?" I said, leading him on.

The lawyer's eyes lit up. "A bigger bundle than you ever made in one season."

It was pretty tempting, but I had to turn him down. It would've spoiled all my fun. I must admit that I get a big kick out of reading about my evil ways. Besides, it's money in my pocket. The more people talk and write about my slicky pitch, the more effective I get. I just want to lead the league every year in psyche-outs.

Let me tell you about all the different substances I've used trying to keep myself wet and wonderful in the big leagues.

Back in the finger-licking days before the rule change, I tested all kinds of chewing gum to spark my sputum. I heard a lot of fellows swear by Beechnut, but I leaned to Wrigley's Spearmint myself. Maybe I kind of had a soft spot for Wrigley's because of Mr. Wrigley owning the Chicago Cubs. I always got a little extra kick out of using his gum to help beat his baseball team.

But I found out that while Wrigley's worked great for a short time, it just didn't hold up when batters began stepping out of the box on me. I'd dry out too fast from chewing-gum juice.

So for me, in the spitter days, the best thing was slippery elm tablets, or little slivers of bark from the elm. You can buy the tablets at most neighborhood drug stores. It's just a pill about the size of a dime. You let it work in your mouth. Sometimes you can go three innings on one tablet. It sort of has a sweet burnt wood smell-taste. That's the best way I can describe it. There are 24 lozenges in a box. A box costs 29 cents, or about 3 cents a game.

I guess you can call this a free plug. But the advertisement on the box is interesting: "Thayers Slippery Elm. . . Nature's Gentle Demulcent. . . Use freely. Excellent for children as well as adults. Two of these all-vegetable lozenges dissolved in the mouth will produce a smooth, soothing coating that gives quick comfort to irritated throats and helps relieve coughs due to common colds. . . Prepared according to a formula more than 90 years old by the Henry Thayer Company, makers of fine pharmaceuticals since 1847. . . Contains powdered slippery Elm Bark."

I'm not one to take sick, anyway. But when I went on elm, I don't recall ever getting a sore throat. And I sure did like the side effects on the ball.

I wasn't totally dependent on the Henry Thayer Company. I went down to my daddy's farm the winter of 1965, right after I learned the spitter, and chipped me some elm bark. I stowed it in a canister to dry out over the winter. That worked fine, too. But, if you didn't seal it up tight, you'd pick up the odors of wherever it dried. I practiced chewing it while doing chores on the farm just to see its effect on me. A few times, it made me feel like throwing up. But to be successful at anything, you have to pay the price.

I overcame the problem. I took a sliver of elm about the size of an aspirin and rolled some bubble gum around it. That way, it tasted better and was hidden from the umpires.

I tried sea moss, which tended to foam and could

41

make you look like a mad dog on the mound; basswood and chokeberry bark, which you could find back home in Farm Life, North Carolina; and chewing tobacco, which was good if you wanted to throw a "brown spitter." I couldn't take to the tobacco. Maybe growing up planting and harvesting the stuff spoiled my taste for it. I've never cared to chew or smoke.

Once the rules were changed in 1968, I didn't have to worry about saliva any more. The "pure" spitter was dead, but anybody who had money in petroleum jelly stocks must have made some quick profits. Petroleum jelly became many pitchers' best friend in 1968, although some of my compatriots had been testing Vaseline and greasy hair tonics.

I never saw John Wyatt, who used to pitch in Kansas City, but I understand he could make a ball go every way but normal.

Orlando Pena, once a teammate of Wyatt's, remembers him vividly. "He had grease all over his uniform," Pena recalls. "You know how some guys keep a couple of uniforms so they've always got one clean? Well, Wyatt kept a couple of uniforms so he'd always have one *dirty* —one filled with grease. That son-of-a-gun hated to get a uniform washed.

"One time the manager, Hank Bauer, asked Wyatt to sit down next to him in the dugout. I wasn't there, but I heard that Wyatt sat down and slid right off the bench. He was a human grease ball."

Vaseline worked best for me, but I also tried baby oil, suntan lotion and a few brands of hair tonic. The whole idea is to use something that makes the ball drop, but is clear (so it won't stain the ball) and odorless (so you can't smell anything—unless you're Billy Martin).

It was this search—for the perfect clear, odorless substance—that led me to take K-Y vaginal jelly out of the bedroom and put it on the ball field. It was recommended by Dr. Maurice Luke, my family doctor in San Mateo,

California. I told him my requirements, and he told me about K-Y. One of the best things about it was that it dried fast, almost by the time it reached the plate. That was good for keeping my secret from umpires, but it was bad for keeping a handy supply on the mound. If I had a long inning, my K-Y reserves could run pretty low. I had to give up vaginal jelly.

So Vaseline it was, at first one one-ounce tube per game. But as my skill improved, I got down to one tube every three or four games. Funny thing was, I used to carry the tube in my jacket pocket, figuring I couldn't get in too much trouble if I got caught with it. After all, getting caught with Vaseline isn't the same thing as getting caught with the old slippery elm. I mean, it says right on the Vaseline tube: "Soothes chapped skin. . . temporarily soothes minor burns. . . helps prevent diaper rash." I could always claim I was carrying Vaseline for a skin rash. (But, just to be safe, I always told the batboy to be on the alert in case I dropped my tube. Once I slid into home plate and hit the catcher. He went one way, I went the other, and the batboy dove in-between, hunting for the tube. He found it—and I rewarded him with a steak dinner.)

I ought to mention that there are other things you can do to the ball besides wet it up and slick it up. You can scuff it up and cut it up, too, though not like they could in the old days when the owners and the umpires weren't so generous about putting new balls in play. Oldtimers used to cut up balls with filed-down belt buckles and scratch them up with emery and slick them up with paraffin wax, or so I've heard. That sort of thing doesn't quite go on any more, but everybody tries to scuff up a ball now and then.

I remember a few years ago, facing the Phillies, ninth inning, bases loaded, two out, a three-and-two count on Richie Allen (which was his National League name). That was the perfect spot for a scuffer. Sure enough, my infielders

43

came through for me. I made a pick-off throw to first base. Willie McCovey dropped the throw—on purpose. As he picked it up, he scraped it against the dirt around first base, giving me a beautiful scuffer. I signaled the catcher, Dick Dietz, that something unusual was on the way. Then I wound up and threw as hard as I could for the center of the plate. The ball twisted and jumped in about six different directions all at once. Allen swung, and I swear he missed by a foot. Then he stared at me. "You serious?" he said.

"What's the matter, pardner?" I said.

Tom Gorman, the plate umpire, said, "Let me see the ball. I don't believe it." Gorman looked at the ball. On one side it was as bumpy as a popcorn ball. But what could he do? The game was over. "I'll be watching you," Gorman warned me.

I liked what Allen said better. He said, "That ball belongs in the Hall of Fame."

Orlando Pena made a comeback in 1973. He returned to the major leagues at the age of thirty-eight—thanks mostly to a pitch he calls a "Cuban fork ball." It is not a dry pitch. Orlando also has thrown a pitch called the "bubble-gum" ball.

"I mix tobacco with a piece of gum and chew it good," Orlando explains. "Tastes like sweet tobacco. When you blow a bubble with that mixture, anybody who sees it wants to throw up. I knew guys playing winter ball in Cuba who would put a spot of gum right on the ball. Every time the umpire found it, he would throw out the ball. But you could win a ball game in a tight spot with it.

"I tried it once, back in 1958. Willie Miranda was at bat. I stuck a little bit of bubble gum to the ball. And I was feeling pretty good. Pretty confident. So I threw it and he hit a shot that almost took my head off. I'll never know how he ever hit that drop."

That was the first I ever heard of the bubble gum ball.

But there are two balls I know about that I'll bet Orlando Pena and most people never heard: the "stocking ball" and the "tape ball." You had to grow up with me and my brother Jim to know about them.

4

In the beginning, I didn't want to be Bobby Feller.

I wanted to be Gene Autry.

My earliest memories are wanting to be a cowboy—and eating my mom's North Carolina country cooking. She always cooked "from the bottom up," as she put it. The fruit pies, biscuits and cakes were started in the flour barrel. Meat came from our smokehouse. Collards, carrots, beans, blackeyed peas and other vegetables came to flower in our garden. We didn't need the city for anything to keep our stomachs full.

I'll never forget watching her scurrying around every morning. She'd get up at four o'clock, get a bushel basket of laundry out of the way and start cooking. Pretty soon, she had the evening meal—maybe salted backbone pork chops (with the vertebrae attached) with collard greens, cornmeal dumplings, bacon and ice potatoes—simmering in a pot on top of the wood-burning stove.

Before noon, Mamma would scoop me up off the floor like I was a sacrifice bunt and hoist me onto her shoulder. My brother Jim, two years older than me, would pick up a sack of sandwiches. And out we would go to the tobacco field Daddy and the mules had been working since dawn.

Jim and I went along because we were too young to be left alone. We'd watch Mom and Dad sweating and grunting over the crops, row after row until dark, day after day.

I remember, too, the honking oogha horn, and backfiring and jerking along in Daddy's 1934 Ford jalopy, going some ten miles into Williamston, North Carolina, for the Saturday matinees at the Watts picture show. We'd come in smoking like Jack Benny's old Maxwell. We'd take in the double-feature cowboy films and the current serial. My daddy loved the shoot-'em-up westerns. We'd talk about them all week until the next Saturday matinee. I thought a lot about Roy Rogers and Johnny Mack Brown. But Gene Autry was a little slicker in my book. Someday I wanted to be a cowboy like Autry. During those years, I couldn't care less that the St. Louis Cardinals won three straight National League pennants, or that Joe DiMaggio hit safely in 56 games or that Ted Williams batted .406 for a whole season.

I never dreamed about being a big-league ballplayer then, any more than I could imagine that Gene Autry would ever get old, drink something called Bloody Marys and some day own a major-league baseball team in California called "the Angels." And that maybe I'd drive him to another Bloody Mary or two.

Down in North Carolina, the big leagues seemed a long way away. If anybody had ever suggested that someday I'd meet Gene Autry, and wonderful people like Billy Martin and Chris Pelekoudas and Chuck Tanner, I wouldn't have known what they were talking about.

47

Sitting in the fields, Jim and I would talk and daydream away those hot summer days.

"Gaylord? You wanna be a cowboy someday?"

"Yessiree, James. You?"

"No, Gaylord. A ballplayer. Daddy and I were talking. He wanted to be a professional ballplayer when he was a boy but couldn't because of the farm."

"Well then, how can you ever be one?"

"By practicing ball just as hard as you work in the tobacco field, Daddy says."

"I'd rather be like Gene Autry," I said.

"Daddy says that if you are good enough to be a professional ballplayer, you can go on to be anything else you want."

"It sounds like a hard way to become a cowboy. Anyway, what professional ballplayer do you want to be?"

"They say Daddy and Slim Gardner's the best around here."

"Mom won't let you anyway."

Jim and I never solved too much on those hot and sultry summer afternoons in Farm Life, N.C., a community of tenant farms just 35 miles south from Ahoskie, about a two-hour walk east of Williamston (pop. 6570) and about an hour's drive north of Greenville.

It was so hot sitting in that boiling sun, your britches would burn the tops of your legs if you didn't move around. So we'd pitch stones at trees or hit clods of mud with dead tree limbs. The only relief was an occasional wisp of cool salt air from the ocean, about 90 miles to the east. It was the same wind that brought the hurricanes up from the Gulf. The hurricanes kept the farmers around those parts in debt and sharecropping for generations.

To a little farm boy, the smell of salt air meant pirates and buried booty. Folks around home talked of Calico Jack, Edward Teach, the infamous Blackbeard, Stede Bonnet, Long Ben, Captain Kidd and Jack Ketch. They all poked in and out of the coves along the Carolina coast and some even sneaked inland up the Roanoke River near Williamston. Stede Bonnet was said to have buried a hoard of three million Spanish dollars and pieces of eight on the Outer Banks near Cape Hatteras. Treasure hunts broke out all over the eastern Carolinas when a small chest filled with gold coins was unearthed on Oak Island in the fall of 1938. It sort of shifted the local spotlight from my birth on September 15 that year.

I was named Gaylord—down home they pronounce it "GAY-lerd"—after my daddy's best friend who had died after having his teeth pulled.

My daddy walked for hours that night in the fields under the clear light of a full harvest moon. He was thankful to the Good Lord for bringing him another son because more sons meant he could rent more land some day. He traded in his 1934 Chevy on a "new" 1934 Ford. The tobacco leaves were turning yellow-green and about ready for the first pulling. It looked like a good crop. Maybe, Daddy thought, he could pay off some of his debts along with the $35 it cost to have me delivered into the world. Nineteen years later, I turned over to Daddy about $30,000 of my bonus money when I signed with the Giants—the equivalent of ten years of income from the peanuts, corn and tobacco we raised. "Gaylord turned out to be one of the best investments I ever made," says Daddy.

I was the middle one of my folks' three children. Jim was two years older, sister Carolyn seven years younger. "I'd love to have had more children," Daddy says, "but we decided we had to stop there. We couldn't take the chance on having another girl. Not when you have bills to meet. You need strong sons to help you get in your crops."

You could trace Daddy's uneasiness back to his birth, August 11, 1919. His daddy, James, died shortly before he was born and his mother died giving birth to him and his twin sister. The twin passed away from disease before she was two years old. Daddy was brought up by his Aunt Lucy and Uncle Amos. Daddy saw nothing but tree stumps to pull out, planting and harvesting, all by mule, from the time he was five years old. I guess that's why he wanted things to be different for us. (Jim and I didn't start mule-plowing until we were *seven* years old.) Dad took to sports and he was outstanding, but it wasn't easy. He lived four miles from school and he'd practice football and baseball afternoons and have to walk home and right into the fields to tend the crops. Uncle Amos cared little for sports and kind of resented Dad's playing when there was work to be done. The three years Daddy played for Williamston High, they won 21 of 22 football games. Daddy had a chance to pitch for a Class D minor-league team, but had to pass it up because he couldn't leave the farm work to Uncle Amos.

He gave up a professional sports career and married Ruby Coletrain, a Farm Life girl he had known for three years. He left his foster home at the age of eighteen and took a tenant farm of his own on land belonging to Asa Roberson. Daddy put his life savings of $125 into the wood-burning stove and some furniture. He confined his baseball to the semipro league. They had to pass the hat to collect money for equipment and never had more than two base-balls for a whole game. The game ended if both balls were lost.

They're still talking about Daddy back home. They say he ran with a football good enough to go professional. And he could pitch a baseball that kept most of the minor-league barnstorming teams out of the Farm Life area. They talk about Daddy and Slim Gardner, a pitcher six-foot-six with no teeth but a fast ball they said could match a bolt of lightning.

Once, against New Bern, N.C., Slim, the story goes, pitched both ends of a July 4th doubleheader. He shut out the New Bern Bears in the morning game, had a big barbecue lunch, swam the mile-wide Neuse River and then shut out the Bears again that afternoon. He and Daddy pitched for the Farm Life team in the semipro Beaufort County League. It wasn't anything for Daddy to come out of the fields and pitch back-to-back games. They still talk about a day back in 1941, the hottest day in local history, over 110 degrees. Daddy pitched Farm Life to a 4–1 victory over White Post in the first game and came right back with another complete game, 9–3.

Dad had some speed and a good curve he wasn't afraid to use on a 3-and-2 count. He had fine control, and his knuckler was as good as Hoyt Wilhelm's, they said. Daddy knew nothing about the spitter. But ol' Slim knew something. I remember one time Slim calling to me. I was just old enough to plow then. "Gaylord," he said, kind of softlike through his gums, "how'd you like to see somethin' unusual with a baseball?"

It was something for a man of Slim's stature in the community to talk to you. I said eagerly, "Yes sir, Mr. Gardner."

He bounced that wad of chew in his cheek as big as a tennis ball and squeezed a wad of spit from his mouth. Pa-too-ey. He let it go right into the pocket of his glove. He took the ball and rubbed one half of it hard into the glove, took it out and then threw it. The ball dipped into his catcher's foot and split his toenail in two. The boy started hopping around like a one-legged rooster. He was expecting the throw somewhere up around his waist.

"That's my tobacco ball, Gaylord. If you ever become a pitcher, it'll help you. C'mon, I'll fix one up for you. Try it."

What could I do? He juiced one up again and handed it to me and I thought I was gonna throw up. It was slimy and I couldn't wait to throw it to somebody just to get it out of my hand. He laughed at the prank he had pulled on me. I never used Slim's tobacco ball, but I loved to watch him pitch. The only thing I liked more was to watch Slim chew tobacco with no teeth.

Baseball was everything when Jim and I were growing up. It was work the fields, go to worship on Sunday and play ball. Baseball stirred the soul, like a religion. The tradition of the game down home produced the community pitcher, a highly respected man comparable to the town parson, the corner druggist and the community Confederate Army veteran. Slim Gardner and Evan Perry, my dad, were much respected.

Daddy believes both he and Slim could have made the big leagues. "But times where so tight during the depression," Daddy recalls. "Being a poor farmer kept you down. In those days, you did what your folks told you to do. Young boys didn't just take off like they do nowadays."

Most of the year, a tobacco farmer spent five days a week, "can till can't" (from the time you *can* see the sun, until the time you *can't*), and a half day on Saturday if he was going to keep his tenancy on a little spit of land. But Daddy made up his mind the day we were born that there would always be time for Jim and me to play some ball, no matter how much field work needed to be done.

One of the first times Jim and I were playing catch, a high throw came down on me like a bomb. It hit me in my two front teeth. Daddy drove me to the dentist, who took out both teeth—barehand—and gave Daddy a bill for $4. "Four dollars?" he said. "Why, I could have done that back in the kitchen for nothing!"

Early in 1946, I was given the reins of our two plow mules, Mollie and Red. It was my first grown-up responsibility on the farm. I was plowing the same way folks had done it for two hundred years. The same as when the Griffins, Robersons, Mannings, Peeles and Biggs came from England to settle Farm Life under the grant of King George. My first steps plowing were a thrill. But it only took me a couple of rows behind a pair of mules for the thrill to end. The next thing I learned was to watch where I stepped.

With jet planes from Myrtle Air Force Base going as fast as the speed of sound in the skies overhead, Jim and I and Daddy and Mamma were bent over at the waist tending the crops barehanded and barefooted. Carolyn, only a baby, was sleeping in a basket in the shade of a magnolia tree. Our farming was primitive.

Our only diversion was playing baseball for an hour during our lunch. We had a bat, a ball we made ourselves and Daddy's glove. The pitcher never wore the glove. And we'd rotate pitching, shagging the ball and hitting.

Mom would shake her head and holler: "Evan? Evan, you and the boys are blamed fools playin' ball in this awful heat when you should be restin'."

"Ruby," said Daddy. "The boys work and go to church. The least they can do is learn how to play baseball. They need to learn it. It'll give 'em some fun when they grow up. There's no telling where ball can take 'em, if they're good enough."

Not one of the elder Perrys could have dreamed then that both of their scrawny young sons would someday play ball from California to Washington, D.C., both be voted best pitchers in the world in separate seasons and barnstorm as far away as Europe and Japan.

Mom helped us with the ball making. One we used was a stocking ball. It was old socks rolled tightly into a round wad and sewn together. It was good because it was firm enough to hit but you didn't have to chase it so far. To make a "regular ball" we'd use a walnut, rock or hard rubber ball for the core. We would get some yarn from Mamma and wind it up tight until it got the size of a regulation ball. Then we'd wrap it over with some black tar tape.

We always had a bat of some kind, all taped and nailed together. Sometimes, we'd use an old oak root. And Mamma, even as busy as she was, would sew up some old fertilizer sacks for uniforms.

The neighborhood farm kids would tease us. "Hey," they'd say, "you boys play ball like you smell."

"Yeah, you both stink!"

We learned baseball the way it should be learned: by playing it for fun. Daddy was our pitcher. We used the potato barn for a backstop, and we devised our own rules: you were out when the ball was caught on a fly and you kept score by how far the ball was hit.

When we got older, we got together with some other Farm Life boys and cleared a pasture to make a ball field. One of the neighborhood tenant farmers loaned us some land, and we used our mules to clear and scrape off an infield. Somebody gave us some pine logs which we took to the saw mill and cut up for a backstop and bleachers. Neighbors gave us money and chickens and hogs to go toward buying equipment.

When we were about fourteen years old, Jim and I joined Daddy on the Farm Life semipro team. We were big for our age, so we got an early start. Daddy pitched, of course, and Jim and I played infield and outfield. The Farm Life team was made up of three families mostly: the Griffins, the Hardesons and the Perrys.

There was no Little League baseball then. We had none of that so-called expert coaching that the youngsters are getting today. Our best coaching came from Dad. He said, "Keep your eye on the ball when you're batting" and "Throw strikes when you're pitching." That might sound a little basic. But I'll bet you a jar of Vaseline you'll hear that repeated at least once on some major-league club every day of the season. Actually, I never was taught anything really technical about the game until I pitched semipro down in Texas in 1957. Jim and I were lucky in two ways at Farm Life (and later at Williamston High): no improper coaching that might have ruined our young arms and no pressure from Mom and Dad to win. We just pitched until we got tired. And a desire to win just developed naturally. We never had the fancy uniforms and manicured lawn fields the city boys had. But we outplayed them. At one time not long ago, there were 25 boys from our county playing pro ball.

I'll always remember those Farm Life ball games against towns like Edenton, Ahoshie, Tarboro and Hertford (Catfish Hunter's town). People came on horses, in buggies and gas jalopies and on foot. They brought food and soft drinks for after-the-game picnic spreads, win or lose.

54

Some days we'd get as many as a thousand people at a game, all up and down the foul lines and beyond the outfield. There was no fighting and no moonshine drinking that I saw. It was a nice crowd of people who came out to cheer the community club and rib the visiting team. But when the game was on the line, you'd hear the people yelling "Here's five dollars for a hit," or "Here's five dollars for a strikeout," or "Two live chickens if you bring in a run!" And after the game, we'd pass the hat and collect some money for equipment, and whatever was left we divided up. When we got older, we'd pick up as much as twenty dollars for pitching a victory and maybe ten dollars if we lost. That sure helped out at home.

Jim drove the school bus to help out the family and I washed dishes at Griffin's Quick Lunch for a dollar an hour. It's the hub and the heartbeat of little Williamston, a meeting ground for everybody from the preacher, mayor and police chief to the boys down on their luck. I don't remember being a model employee. I spent more time eating than I did washing dishes.

Daddy, Jim and I played together until I was seventeen years old. Daddy pitched as good at forty as he did when he was twenty-eight. I guess that's why Jim and I have held up so long. Daddy taught us to take good care of ourselves.

"Gaylord? James? Time to get your feet on the ground," Mamma called. The sun was still hidden. Jim and I would start to stretch in our bed. We'd bump into each other most every morning. I never had a bed of my own until Jim went off to junior college. But it wasn't so bad being in one bed in the winter, especially since the house wasn't quite sealed against the wind and one time Blanche, who was my girl friend then, asked me about a big hole in the floor of my bedroom. "Gaylord, why don't you and Jim nail shut that hole?" she said. "It's letting in

55

all the cold from outside." I explained that there was a whole lot more draft coming through the window and walls, anyway. All we could do was just bury ourselves in feather-quilt blankets and let our body heat do the rest.

"Gaylord? James? C'mon, get some while it's hot. I got some surprises out here waiting," Mamma would call again. It'd be sweet biscuits or something she'd made to feed our sweet tooth. That'd always get us into our farm clothes quicker. The house had no bathroom. We'd wash up on the back porch with a basin of cold water, lard soap Mamma made and a wash cloth. That was our morning and nightly "bath." On Saturday nights, we might boil up water on the wood stove and fill a big old tub. If you took pretty good care of yourself all week with the wash cloth, you might get two baths out of one load of water on Saturday night.

I never could have dreamed then that someday I'd be living in a suite at the Waldorf Astoria Hotel in New York City with indoor plumbing, shower-bath and more room than in that whole farmhouse. There are very few things a boy coming off a tenant farm will ever take for granted.

When Jim and I were growing up, our house was already a century old. My father-in-law, Asa J. Manning, was born there. Some of the houses were lived in by a single family for generations, going back before the Civil War. Our place was built with heart pine lumber, a yellow-pine siding that's never been painted to this day. Heart pine turns grayish-brown with age and has natural protection against weathering. The house had no basement and it was built up off the ground to keep snakes and insects from nesting underneath. It had four large rooms, two on each side of a wide hall that went front to back. There was Mom and Dad's bedroom, mine and Jim's, and Carolyn's. The front room was the living room. It was kept locked and reserved for company. It had all our fancy things like pictures, souvenir ashtrays, fancy stuffed furniture and little statues and things Daddy won at the county fairs pitching baseballs.

The carnival man would see us coming and tell daddy, "Now, Evan Perry, I've got a right to make a living, too. I'm gonna have to cut you off when you have something for everybody in your family."

Daddy'd just smile and say, "Here's a dime, Zeke, give me the balls. My arm feels pretty snappy today." Zeke groaned. And soon a crowd would gather watching Daddy winding up like he was on the mound and blasting those milk bottles off the stand. Everything he won wound up in the living room.

There was a second floor to the house, but it was kept locked. We couldn't afford to heat it. About 200 feet in back was the outhouse. When the weather got cold, it was no fun. And when you had to make a trip out there in the middle of the night, it didn't do you any good to think about some of the ghost legends of eastern North Carolina.

There's one story about old Joe Baldwin. They say the ghost of Old Joe prowls the railroad tracks at night carrying a yellow lantern. He is supposed to have been wandering the tracks since 1863 when he fell from a train and got his head cut off. They say that bobbing yellow lantern seen after midnight is Old Joe trying to find his head. President Grover Cleveland came through eastern Carolina once and claimed he'd seen the light flickering in the night. Trainmen carry two lanterns so they won't be mistaken for Old Joe's ghost and invite a load of buckshot in the seat of the pants. I was coming back to the house pulling up my britches one night when I saw one yellow light bobbing in the woods and coming toward me. I wish somebody had a stopwatch on my dash from there to the house, while holding up my pants with one hand.

In the kitchen, we had running water coming from a single faucet. The water ran out through a drain pipe onto the ground. It was a simple house with simple, usable furniture. But it was spotless. Mamma and Daddy were perfectionists. We didn't have many clothes—I wore Jim's hand-me-downs until I got as big as he was—but we were always extra clean.

Out in the yard, there were two tobacco barns about 30 by 30 feet square and about that tall. The barns had wood-burning ovens to dry out the tobacco that we would stack to the rafters across wood sticks. Then we had sheds for the corn and hay, one each for the mules, hogs and chickens, and the potato and smokehouses where Daddy stored our vegetables and meat. That was the farm. We had a community phone with our own ring. That was our only contact with the neighbors. The nearest ones lived a mile away.

When Jim and I were growing up, Daddy was share-cropping for Asa and Irene Roberson. The landlord gave him the house, two mules, the farming equipment and 25 acres of cleared land. Dad had to furnish the house inside, grow the crops and keep up the farm. He split the cost of seed and fertilizers. And one-half of everything the crops brought in went to the landowner. Daddy raised corn and peanuts. But tobacco was the main money crop. We raised the hogs and chickens for ourselves. We grew our own vegetables and Mamma made most of our clothes. We didn't need much to live on maybe because we learned how to go without. In a good year, Daddy would clear between $3000 and $4000. But one bad hurricane would set a man back five years. He might never catch up.

At early morning breakfast, we never thought about the work we had to do or the bills we owed. Daddy, Jim and I never looked at a day of farm work with dread. It was something you had to do to eat. Dirt farming taught you to think about what you were doing right then, never ahead to all the work waiting for you that day, that week or for the rest of your life.

The kerosene lamps gave the kitchen a soft brightness.

58

We didn't have electricity. The spread on the breakfast table was enough for ten men. But we always put a pretty good dent in the eggs, ham and bacon, some pork, hot biscuits and homemade jellies, milk and steaming hot coffee. We would talk over the schedule for the day's work. It was then that Jim and I would start our daily campaign for substituting hunting and fishing for farming. We'd tell Dad about the black bear seen two farms away and how it had killed a henhouse full of chickens. We hoped Dad would take the bait and give us a shorter work day to do some hunting. And the same with fishing. We'd tell him how good they were biting at Mill Creek. He'd just smile and compliment us for our excellent hunting and fishing report. Then he'd outline the day's work.

After breakfast, we'd go to the barn, hitch Mollie and Red to the wagon and head for the fields. We would be out there before seven o'clock. Jim recalls, "I was always faster at working the crops than Gaylord. We'd start out together and I'd soon end up a row ahead of him. 'Course, I was older. Next to his being slow, the thing I remember about Gaylord is that he sucked his thumb until he was nine. He'd come in after working all day on the farm and his whole hand would be black but his thumb would still be white."

Daddy marveled at my farming. "I never saw a boy sweat so much as Gaylord, whether in the fields barefoot or walking to school. I guess learning to sweat on the farm helped him with his pitching." We would work until dusk, play some ball until dark, eat a giant country meal, listen to the radio and be in bed by about nine o'clock. We had no trouble sleeping. There was nothing better for growing up and family togetherness than working a farm. I wasn't away from the farm one day of my life until the time I went away to play baseball the summer between my junior and senior years at Williamston High.

I believe the long hot hours in the fields gave Jim and me a physical and mental discipline that has helped us on the mound. (Honest sweat, and a little Vaseline, has always been one of my best friends.) Dad's theory was, "Do for yourself or do without."

The folks down home always considered the Perry boys very serious for their age. We had so little free time, once we started our schooling. But before I got involved in football and basketball in high school, the winters were wonderful times. At home, we'd listen to Bill Stern sports and the Friday night fights, "Amos and Andy," "The Lone Ranger" and "Gangbusters" on our battery radio. Mom would heat up some popcorn or roast some chestnuts and Dad might get out the checkerboard.

Sometimes Dad would take Jim and me to Noah Roberson's grocery store where us kids would sit quietly around the wood-burning pot-bellied stove and listen to the older folks. They'd recall some of Dad's big games or some Slim Gardner stories. They'd talk about Jimmy Brown, a local boy who played with the St. Louis Cardinals in the 1930s and 40s. World War topics would come up and some wondered what the Russians were after. There were some Russian families in the area and they all seemed nice enough, the folks agreed.

But I loved to hear Revolutionary War tales of the Edenton Tea Party. It happened *before* the Boston Tea Party. Mrs. Penelope Barker and some North Carolina women pulled off the same thing first right in North Carolina. Maybe the only cavalry-naval battle ever fought happened near Williamston. General Robert E. Lee's army was being supplied over a bridge crossing the Roanoke River. A Union Army gunboat came up the river to blow up the bridge, and a Confederate cavalry unit engaged the boat from the shoreline.

There were some great tales about the shipwrecks along North Carolina's Outer Banks, the graveyard of the Atlantic. The ship Flambeau's cargo of 10,000 stovepipe hats washed ashore all at once in the spring of 1867. The Flambeau was bound for South America when she ran aground and broke apart. The beaches soon were knee-deep in tall beaver hats. The law of finders-keepers was applied, and soon every man, woman and child on Hatteras Island had a stovepipe hat and several spares. The ship owners called in the army to recover their hats.

About 1950, Manning-Gurkin's country store got the first television set in our community. We switched over there from Roberson's store so we could see the wrestling and boxing matches. Our socializing was pretty much confined to the gatherings around the pot-bellied stove, tent revival meetings and picnics at Maple Grove First Christian Church (built by Blanche's granddaddy). And most every Sunday night, the Gurkins, Coletrains and other neighbors would come to the house and play a favorite Carolina card game called, "Catch the Five." Jim and I socialized at the Scout Hut, Noah Roberson's store. A favorite spot was Nathaniel Coletrain's East Side where we'd pull for Cokes. You grab a Coke, turn it up to see where it was bottled and the boy with the one from the farthest away would have his paid for by the other boys.

One of the big moments in the Perry family history was the electrification of our tenant farm in May of 1951, the same time the New York Giants called Willie Mays up from Minneapolis.

Electrification brought broadcasting into the Perry house. First, Daddy bought a used Philco floor cabinet radio. Then, in 1953, we got a brand new 14-inch RCA television, in time to see the New York Yankees beat the Brooklyn Dodgers in the World Series. Somebody named Billy Martin went 12-for-24 for the Yankees.

The Perry family went loony over wrestling. We caught every match we could. We'd get so worked up, we couldn't watch close to meal time. I have to confess I thought all that smashing and slamming was the real thing. I never knew it was a show until I went to spring training with the Giants, in 1959. The first night in camp, I saw my first live wrestling match and I was shocked. I could see it was a phony, but I couldn't bring myself to tell the folks for a couple of years. I hate to spoil people's illusions about pitching or anything.

I'll forever be thankful for my boyhood on the farm. Away from broken bottles and rusting tin cans and the noise of big cities. City boys never get to know the gentleness of a mill creek, or the beauty of deer sniffing around the barns in winter looking for food, or such delicacies as robin and blackbird pie, squirrel pie and rabbit stew, snake and possum. I didn't care much for possum, but a lot of folks do.

I was a big deal in the 4H club and used its membership to get out of class. We raised hogs and judged them. We'd tell Mr. Braswell, our teacher, we were in the next livestock-judging contest. There was Dail Roberson, Buck Manning, J.C. Manning and myself. We talked the teacher into letting us leave the classroom because we needed to practice judging which, of course, is impossible. Anybody knows you can't practice judging without somebody else watching and telling you how good you did.

But Mr. Braswell said, "Sure."

So we all went up to Noah Roberson's store, sat down at the card table and played "Catch the Five" all afternoon. Suddenly, through the door came old Braswell. He didn't know about us. He was sneaking a break himself. He blew his stack but couldn't do too much about it since he couldn't explain how he got there to catch us.

Farm Life, the name of our farming community, came from the name of the school, not the other way around like you might think. Farm Life School was a regular school, but specialized in teaching what boys needed to know about farming. The building was red brick, with four big classrooms. Two grades were taught in each room. One class would work while the other would coast. It was that way right up through the eighth grade. The school had about 120 students.

Whenever our grade was "coasting," I'd ask to be excused to go to the bathroom or first aid room and I'd slip out the window and down a coal pile to a basketball court we had rigged up. One by one, the other boys would follow. I'm sure our teacher knew it, but she was just as happy to have fewer in the room cutting up while she was working the other grade. I was not what you'd call a serious student.

One day playing basketball barefoot, I nearly lost my leg. I ran into a lead pipe that gouged a chunk out of my shin. It was bandaged, but it got infected. At school the next day, I was rushed to the hospital. Gangrene had set in. The doctor told me, "Gaylord, you were just a half a day's more poison from losing that leg."

A year or so later, I nearly lost my hands and my life. I found a bunch of dynamite caps in an abandoned shed. I put the caps on the woodchopping block and hit them with a hand axe. They exploded like fire crackers. I was having a good old time until I hit one cap wrong and it blew to pieces like shrapnel. I got my hands full of it and the force of the blast carried the axe-head right past my ear. It was back to the hospital again.

Daddy was really upset. He told me, "Gaylord, if that happens again and you don't kill yourself, I will." The doctor just marveled at my good luck. He said, "Gaylord, first the lead pipe almost gets you, and now it's a miracle you don't blow yourself up. You are a mighty fortunate young man. There is somebody, somewhere watching out for you!" Whoever he was, I wish he'd come around now and talk to the baseball rules committee.

5

I enrolled at Williamston High School in the fall of 1954, only a few weeks before the Giants and the Indians, my future teams, met in the World Series. Willie Mays was the Series hero, but the hero at Williamston High was my brother Jim. He was a junior, two years ahead of me. Everyone wanted to see what would happen when I teamed up with him.

Entering high school for most teen-age boys meant getting a brand new outfit of clothes, a book bag, a dictionary, some notebooks and a mechanical pencil you had to promise not to lose. Haircuts were a buck and the style was short. Even at the age of sixteen, I had no trouble keeping my hair short.

I'll always remember one Saturday afternoon in early September, just before classes were to begin. We were up at dawn and pulled enough sticks of tobacco to fill up the curing barn by noon. We washed up, and then Daddy said, "C'mon Gaylord, we got to go to town and get you ready for school."

Daddy wanted me properly "attired" when I entered my freshman year. We jumped into our "new" '39 Pontiac and chugged into town to Manning-Peele's Hardware. Manning-Peele's Hardware carried just about everything, from tobacco seeds to ice boxes, from thread to used carburators to vitamins. If Manning-Peele's didn't have it, you didn't need it.

"Evan, you come to fit out Gaylord for school?" A.J. Manning asked Daddy with a twinkle in his eye. A.J. was Blanche's Daddy, my future father-in-law.

"Yep. I want you to fix him up, A.J."

"Well, we got in these nice new fielding gloves from Wilson Sportin' Goods. Most of the boys like them. Nowadays the boys go for any glove that catches a ball for them. Gaylord? You can net catfish with this one."

A.J. turned to Dad. "Not like when you started, is it, Evan?"

"My first ball glove was a canvas work glove," Daddy said. "I toughened it up with sticky road tar. It wasn't big. But the ball sure stuck."

I smacked my fist into the stiff new glove. I was going to be a third baseman. The glove had no endorsement on it. It wasn't the kind any player would put his name to. But it was my pride and joy. My own first glove. It cost Daddy $5.25.

"You want us to wrap it or you want to wear it?" Mr. Manning laughed. He knew I'd want to wear it.

Daddy smiled up at me. He said, "Does it fit good? Fine. Now we got to get some shoes for the boy's feet. Better fit them extra long. He's growing so fast he gains a size by the time we get him home from the store."

Right behind the hip boots and rubber raincoats were the shoes I needed. Mr. Manning said, "Here. These are

65

some genuine college football shoes with removable cleats. I think size thirteen ought to fit, with one extra size for cotton stuffing in the toes."

Daddy said to wrap them up. Now I was ready for my freshman year at Williamston High. Prepared for my first day of higher education—in sports. (I wasn't awe inspiring in the classroom. Getting grades was just one way to "stay in shape" so I could compete.) I'll forever be grateful to Daddy who spent money the family really couldn't spare to buy me shoes and a glove. It turned out to be a good investment for all of us.

Daddy looked out the store window nervously, cleared his throat and mumbled to Mr. Manning, "Put it on our account, A.J." It was the account Daddy had been running for some 20 years. He and A.J. never dwelt on the possibility that Daddy might never be able to pay it off. I promised myself that if I ever could, I'd some day walk into Manning-Peeles with Daddy and close that account. (When I did it, we celebrated at Dullin's Soda Shop with a fountain Pepsi filled with a handful of salted peanuts.)

Williamston High had an enrollment of about 300 students, all of them white when I was there. We didn't ever compete with black athletes. Many times I've wondered how many Hank Aarons and Willie Mays wasted their strength and coordination pulling tobacco and raking peanuts on some little patch of land down home.

Down home, that's where we had separate schools for the blacks, separate toilets, separate sides of the street, and front-and-back buses. The blacks went to their own high school, Edgar J. Hayes. They were better than Williamston in football and played a darned good game of basketball. But they only competed against other black schools.

When integration came to our county, Hayes' pupils moved to Williamston High (Hayes was changed to a grade school) and they lost their separate identity. A lot of folks down home believe the blacks had it better when things were segregated.

I don't buy that. I'm a Southerner, but I sure believe in integration. I ought to. I don't know what I'd have done later on without Willie Mays and Willie McCovey behind me.

A good friend of mine down home was a black man by the name of Annox Peale. He used to help us work the farm. He was a wonderful man, a hard worker, a happy man, even though he'd never really known a vacation in his life. In 1968, a bunch of my friends and I treated Annox to a real vacation.

For years, my good friend Booger Scales, an insurance man from Greenville, had been organizing a North Carolina safari once or twice a season to come see me pitch. Anywhere from a dozen to a busload of friends would roll north to catch me in action. They'd bring Daddy along, too, and make it a big party. Mamma would prepare a feast of country ham and biscuits, barbecue chicken and pork for Daddy to bring to me, everything wrapped in waxed paper so it'd last.

Annox made the trip in 1968. We got him a new suit, shoes and hat and vacation money to spend. Annox was the life of that party. To him, Willie Mays was bigger than the president of the United States. Willie promised me he'd pose for a picture with Annox right on the field. I introduced Annox to Willie, and a photographer came by to snap their picture.

Howard Cosell was standing at home plate. He wanted Willie for an interview for national television. Naturally, it had to start when Howard was ready. In his usual style, he put one hand on his hip and called to Willie. "Wil-lie! Wil-lie Mays, I can't wait all day. Wil-lie Mays. . . One of the all-time greats. Mil-lions of your fans, Wil-lie Mays, are waiting to hear me in-ter-view you. And we can't wait all day. . . Wil-lie. . ."

Willie cut Howard off with a good imitation. "Howard Co-sell. . . Your fans will have to wait. I'm talking with my friend, An-nox. And then, we're going to pose for

67

a picture." For that moment at least, Annox owned the whole world. He told me later he had the best time of his life on that trip. He came down with cancer a year later and it took him fast. We tried to buy him some time with the best medical treatment, but the disease had gone too far. When he died, I cried. His widow keeps an eight-by-ten autographed photo of Annox and Willie right on her TV set, alongside a little vase of cut flowers.

Williamston High was built during the Great Depression. My daddy attended school there. It's a three-story brown brick building with the gymnasium alongside it. When I got there, the school had a winning tradition in all sports except football.

Basketball and baseball were the big sports. It was just too hot to play football in the daytime, and you couldn't pay fans to watch it on a Saturday afternoon. Skewawkee Park had no lights. It was named after James Skewawkee, a colonel in the Revolutionary War. We played football and baseball there. The football field was laid out across the ball field, giving it the look of the old Polo Grounds, sideways. Some called it an all-purpose field. The way it was laid out, it had no purpose I could tell. But it got Jim and me a load of college scholarship offers and two professional baseball contracts, and that wasn't bad for old Skewawkee.

We Perry boys were the tallest around then. Jim and I were both about six-foot-three. Jim already was rated one of the best pitchers and centers in the state in baseball and basketball. I was expected to be as good, and was I ever anxious to get started.

I'll always remember the first day of school. P.C. Bryant, our agriculture teacher, took me under his wing. He handed out questionnaires. Under the column "What do you want to be?" I wrote down as heavily as I could, "Professional Baseball Player." I guess they all thought that was a little unusual since most of the boys wrote

"Doctor," "Lawyer," "Sheriff," "Farmer" or something solid.

"Gaylord, don't you have a real job in mind for yourself?" P.C. asked.

"Yessiree, playing baseball for cash."

"Well, just how you gonna be sure anybody'll pay you for it?"

"By practicing every spare chance I get. Daddy says I can make it if I work hard enough."

My first exposure to organized sports was the Williamston High football team. I had never played a game of football in my life. The only thing I knew was tossing the ball around and catching it. I must have looked like something from the day of the drop kick and the flying wedge. I had an old leather helmet with loose ear flaps that sat too small on the top of my head. I wore the brand new high-top football shoes Daddy got me and baggy canvas pants the school lent me. Williamston was just changing over to plastic helmets and snug uniforms. But, as a freshman, I was on the bottom of the list for new equipment.

When the coach, Roger Thrift, handed out the plays we were going to use, they looked to me like pirate treasure maps. The O's and X's were so puzzling, I carried them around in my hip pads, so I could get to them fast when I needed them.

The first few workouts, I tried out at halfback and quarterback. I was sneaking a peek at my route on the next play when Coach Thrift came up behind me and blew on his whistle so hard my ears quivered. But I wasn't so startled that I didn't catch my falling helmet before it hit the ground.

"Perry?" the coach demanded, "just how much do you know about football?"

"I'm starting from scratch, Coach."

"Well why don't you forget the plays and just be a defensive end?"

"Fine, what do I do?"

"You just stand here and if anybody comes by with

69

the ball you grab him. And there will be some guys trying to block you, so you fight them off."

That I understood. I was so excited I couldn't wait for somebody to come my way. The varsity offense started running plays at me. I just waded through the blockers and leveled the ball carrier. I kept the practice running late that first day. Coach Thrift was upset because they couldn't run his simple plays around me. I guess he figured if they couldn't run over a green freshman end, they couldn't against Tarboro or Edenton.

The seniors complained to me, "Look, you keep tackling like that and Coach is gonna keep us out here all day. Kinda fake it." That really teed me off. I just couldn't let myself give in like some of those guys. I was even more determined. So day after day I kept busting up everybody. I figured I could make the starting team by the process of elimination. Soon everybody else was hurting, which made it look like I was improving. I began to impress Coach Thrift.

By the third game, I had made starting defensive end. Coach Thrift wanted me to go in there and "bust 'em up." Mamma and Daddy were in the stands and like any kid I wanted to show them I was pretty good. On my first play, Edenton High ran my way, and I hit the ball-carrier so hard he almost came out of his uniform. The officials gave me a 15-yard penalty for unnecessary roughness.

Later that season, I got to play some offense. Until I learned the pass patterns, I'd just run out between the defensive backs and wave for the ball. But I must have had some talent because the colleges started to come around to talk scholarship when I got to be a junior.

I enjoyed football. But I have to admit that the only times in my life I ever bugged out on practices were in football. One time was in my sophomore year. A portable roller skating rink came to Williamston. It was laid out under a circus tent. Several of us "athletes" were dying to try it out before it moved on to the next town. I never had roller skated in my life. Coach Thrift put it off-limits: "I don't want you boys falling down and injuring yourself." Four of us told him one day we weren't feeling well and would like to go home to rest. Then we took off for the roller rink, rented some skates and went wild on the boards. We were all hooting and hollering, banging into each other and falling down. I was showing off my new trick of skating on one foot with the other waving out in front of me. I yelled, "Watch this gang. Whooooeee."

Suddenly, there was a burst of applause from the front of the rink. Somebody yelled, "Gaylord, you are the greatest. You're almost good enough to be on the television."

It was Coach Thrift. He had gotten wind of our caper. Without turning around to look at him, we raced to the end of the rink, split open a new rear exit in the canvas tent and took off into the nearby tobacco fields. We made pretty good time, considering we never stopped to take off the skates.

Football coaching was a constant struggle in our farming community. All of us boys had to be in on the harvest in late August and September. That's when the tobacco and peanuts came in. When Coach Thrift came to Williamston in 1953, the realities hit him fast: "I came to Williamston all gung-ho. We were allowed two-a-day practices and I had a program all set up. The first morning workout I called, I had four boys show up. The afternoon workouts weren't much better. Finally, Evan Perry came by the school and said, 'Coach, have one practice a day. I'll round up the kids from Farm Life and drive them up in loads. But they can only make it once. We're in the middle of the tobacco season. And the crops won't wait on you when it's ready for pullin'.' So Williamston worked out when it could. But we were hard-pressed to compete with the city boys in the conference."

Williamston won only four games out of nine in my

71

sophomore season but began to blossom in my junior year. We finished 7–1–1. I was all-state offensive and defensive end, as a sophomore and again as a junior.

In the last game of my junior year against Tarboro, we pulled a double reverse pass play. I came galloping back from my end position and threw a pass they say traveled 50 yards in the air to Jimmy Rodgers in the end zone for a 21–17 victory on the final play of the game. They were talking about moving me to quarterback the next season because I could throw. Nobody ever found out how good I might have been at quarterback.

At the end of my junior year, I was faced with a couple of pretty important decisions. One was whether I should quit playing football; as much as I liked the game, it was already pretty clear my professional future lay in baseball, and an injury could ruin my hopes. The second was whether, instead of going into my senior year at Williamston High, I should shift to Campbell Junior College and finish up there, the way Jim did.

Jim had signed with the Cleveland Indians the summer before. After his classes let out at Campbell in the spring of 1956, he went to Ashboro, N.C. to pitch and work for a hosiery mill that had a semipro ball team. They paid $500 a month. The Yankees, Phillies, Giants and Indians all were after him. Each club, however, wanted him to work out with them for a couple of weeks before a final decision was made. Jim decided against it. He wasn't going to jump all over the country all summer trying to impress teams. He figured that was an easy way to ruin his arm. Finally, the Indians offered him a $4000 bonus and he took it. At that time, the $4000 bonus rule was in effect. If you got more, you had to be placed on the big-league roster for two seasons. Jim didn't want that. He wanted to start at the bottom and *learn* his way to the top. He figured he had a good chance with Cleveland because three of their top pitchers—Early Wynn, Mike Garcia, and Bob Lemon—

were about ready to retire. Jim was assigned to North Platte of the Nebraska State League.

It was generally assumed that, unless I suffered an arm injury, I'd get a pro baseball contract, too. And the money would be a lot bigger because baseball threw out that $4000 bonus rule in 1957. By one year, Jim missed out on as much as $60,000 or $75,000 in bonus money.

The coaching staff at Williamston, my teammates and my classmates didn't want me quitting football, naturally enough.

But all the big-league scouts recommended that I quit playing football and strongly suggested that I finish out my baseball and basketball at Campbell College where the competition would be sharper. The scouts talked about big money. "More than the Perry family could ever imagine," one of them said. I decided to talk it out with Coach Thrift. I was shaking in my shoes as I entered his office.

"Coach," I stammered, "the baseball scouts are after me to quit football. I don't want to let down the team. I'll play if you tell me to."

"Gaylord, I'd never tell you to play."

"Well, I've never really gotten hurt. I don't think the chances are great."

"Gaylord, I don't think you would ever get injured in a game as long as you saw the boy blocking or tackling you. But so many things can happen to you when you're not looking, like being clipped from behind. Something like that could tear up your knee for life. But you have to decide. About that and whether or not to leave Williamston for Campbell College."

Daddy and I spent days walking in the field discussing those decisions. He remembered his own youth, his one chance to play professional ball. He didn't grab it and he never got another. Finally, I decided: my football days

73

were over, but my high school days would end with my graduation from Williamston, not Campbell College.

But I'll never forget my football days, especially my freshman year. Football not only gave me a chance to tackle people, and to block people, it gave me a chance to take a shower, and to use an indoor toilet. For a kid from Farm Life, it was the first taste of culture shock.

6

Now I'm going to tell about my basketball days—with a few digressions here and there. When I got to Williamston High, Jim was already an all-state center. He was nicknamed Goose for some reason, so I got stuck with Duck. Anyway, Jim and I had grown up playing two-on-one basketball against Daddy in the backyard, with a hoop attached to the potato barn. Jim and I knew each other's every move.

Naturally, I was disappointed when, at the start of the season, I was assigned to the junior varsity. I'd been hoping to play with Jim for the first time; he had passed up football. I was really disappointed when I got to know our J.V. coach. The first day of practice, he walked onto the floor with a whistle in one hand and a book in the other. The book was *Playing Winning Basketball* by George

75

Mikan or Bob Cousy or somebody like that. The book was torn and peeling, the ends curling up. Judging from the coach's knowledge, the book must have gotten torn holding up the short leg of an uneven table. The coach sure couldn't have read it.

He told Roger Thrift, who coached varsity basketball as well as football, "Gaylord never will be another Jim. He'll never make it. He can't move quickly enough. And he just doesn't respond to coaching. It'll be a while before he's ready to move up."

For some reason, we never did quite hit it off. At one of our practices, he began telling me how the Boston Celtics brought the ball up the court. He said it was all in the book he was holding.

"Gaylord, the Celtics were disciplined in their ball handling. You'll find that two hands are better than one in any sport. Pass with both hands on the ball. . . . Shoot with both hands on the ball. . . ."

I kept bouncing the ball against the floor while he was lecturing me. The louder he talked, the harder I bounced. The other boys were standing around snickering. All a smart aleck like me needed was an audience. I always had a little ham in me.

"Do you want me to dribble the ball with both hands, too?" I said.

The coach glared at me. "Gaylord," he said, "you don't think much of this book, do you?"

"No, sir," I said. "I liked the movie better."

By the third game of the season, I had worked my way up to regular forward on the varsity. We lost only one game that whole year--to Ahoskie—by one point, 77–76, in the state finals.

My sophomore year, Jim had gone off to college, and Williamston got a brand new gymnasium. Over the entrance to the court was a five-by-ten foot sign bearing this hand-lettered motto:

For when the One Great Scorer comes to write against your name, He marks not that you won or lost, but how you played the game. —GRANTLAND RICE

Just to the left of that message is the door I put my fist through during my junior year. It mattered to me a lot whether I won or lost—*and* how I played the game. We were playing Ahoskie, our arch rivals, and I was having a terrible night. We were far behind in the second period when I fouled out. I was so mad, I slammed my fist through the door. The school principal, B.G. Stewart, leaped from his seat in the stands and came after me waving his fist. "Look what you done! Look what you done!" he screamed. "Our new door!"

Fortunately, P.C. Bryant, who taught shop as well as agriculture, came to my rescue. He promised the door would be repaired as part of a project in shop class.

Fourteen years later, I walked through that gym door again when Jim and I were honored on "Jim and Gaylord Perry Day." That was 1970, some say the best year a pair of pitching brothers ever had in the majors. We became the first brothers ever to oppose each other in an All-Star game. Jim won the Cy Young Award in the American League and I was runner up to Bob Gibson for the award in the National League. Jim won 24 with Minnesota and I won 23 with San Francisco. We became the first brothers ever to win 20 games each in the same season. We fell just two short of the all-time record for victories by a pair of brothers: 49, set by Dizzy (30) and Paul (19) Dean for St. Louis in 1934.

It seems I've always needed a governor on my temper. I take no truck with myself or a teammate when a poor job is done or lack of effort given. Even as a pro, I have that problem. In 1964, the Giants and Houston were tied, 1–1, with two out in the bottom of the ninth, a runner on second and Nellie Fox at bat. Fox hit a grounder that bounced 12 times before it got through the infield. I lost, 2–1. My catcher, Tommy Haller, was so mad he kicked Fox's bat. It landed in front of me. I picked it up and slammed it against the side of the dugout, breaking it in two. Then I handed the top half to the batboy and said, "Here, give this to Fox."

Houston's president, Judge Roy Hofheinz, demanded payment for the broken bat, or he said he'd sue me, Giant president Horace Stoneham, the Giants, the City of San Francisco and the State of California if necessary for the $2.98 bat. National League president Warren Giles pacified Hofheinz with a promise to make the Giants pay the $2.98 and dispatched a telegram to Alvin Dark, then manager of the Giants.

"Tell Perry to stop breaking bats," the wire said. Dark acted instantly. He ordered me, forcing a straight face, "Gaylord, stop breaking bats!"

In my years at Williamston, I was the target of a lot of booing. You especially notice it in basketball with the fans almost on top of you. In the last game of my senior year, we were playing Ahoskie on their court, and the Ahoskie fans never stopped booing me from the moment my name was announced. I scored 42 points and was voted the outstanding player of the tournament. Near the end of the game, I shook hands with every member of the Ahoskie team, right in the middle of a time out. They smiled and slapped me on the back, and even the crowd seemed to be won over. The fans stood up and gave me an ovation.

Finally, the referee had to blow the whistle to get the game going. The instant before the official tossed the ball to me, one Ahoskie rooter stood up and called out clearly: "Perry. . . you *still* stink." Even I had to laugh.

My freshman year at Williamston, I began to notice a beautiful blue-eyed brunette. She was an outstanding straight-A student, played the trombone in the school band, sang in the glee club and read from the Bible in our weekly chapel assembly. She may have been the best female basketball player Williamston ever stuck in bloomers. She once scored 35 points in one game and was all-county two years. She was easily the belle of Williamston High and a much-sought-after dating prospect. She was the same age as I, but she was a grade ahead of me.

Right then, I stopped going to Henry Coletrain, a sharecropper neighbor in Farm Life who used to cut hair for 25 cents a head. The town barbers were getting a buck. Henry "styled" your haircut to the contour of your head. He'd set the comb half an inch off your head and run clippers all over it. If you had bumps on your skull, your hair showed them off. But when Blanche came along, I started to take a closer look at myself in the mirror. I needed a big-league haircut in Williamston from then on.

First time I saw Blanche Manning was the summer before my freshman year. She was dating a friend of Jim's. They had come to the house to double-date with Jim and his girl. I couldn't keep my eyes off her. I was "decked out" in my bib overalls, fresh from shoveling manure, and barefoot. I looked and smelled like something the hogs slept with. The Mannings were well-known folk. The Mannings were way up the social scale from tenant farmers.

Anyway, the moment Blanche, her boy friend and Jim's girl set foot inside the house, Mamma swung into action. Mamma doesn't meet new folks in the normal "how-de-doo." She greets their stomachs.

"I'd like you to meet my mom."

"Pleasure to meet you, Mrs. Perry."

"I'm sorry we don't have some ice cream to go with this," says Mom, offering a plate heaped high with a huge wedge of fresh-baked apple pie or slice of cake.

Daddy is just as hospitable. "Gaylord," he said when Blanche's dating party sat down, "go out to the field and pull us a fresh watermelon."

Out I went. Then Daddy asked me to sweep out the

'39 Pontiac they were going to drive. I even had to help them push to get it started.

Blanche and I got to know each other later through basketball. Williamston played doubleheaders: the girls' varsity team would play the first game and the boys' varsity the second. We rode to out-of-town games together in the team bus. That may seem a little unusual now, but it didn't at the time. Blanche and I would sit in the rear of the bus and talk about the game that night. Blanche and I went to concerts at school. Our favorite musical group was called "The Sunshine Boys." They sang Bible songs. They were darned good, too. Our relationship was what you might call "sportin'-courtin'."

I can't tell what Blanche saw in me those days. But let her tell it: "I sure do remember Gaylord that first meeting. He was built like a giant spider, all arms and legs, elbows and knees, plus big feet and ears that stood out. Basketball gave Gaylord and me a common ground. I guess we did most of our courting on the team bus. We enjoyed record dancing at the Scout Hut and the East Side to Chubby Checkers and Elvis Presley. When Gaylord and I started steady company, my daddy would follow me around and remind me, 'You're not going to ruin that boy's career,' whenever I kept him out late or let him think of something other than baseball. Most every man thinks he could have been a major-leaguer if. . . Daddy did too. He didn't want to see anything stand in Gaylord's way.

"All was fine with us until I graduated and went to Duke University. Gaylord was beginning his senior year at Williamston. Although it was Gaylord and no one else for me, he wouldn't believe it. Our family wasn't wealthy by northern standards. But we had what is called 'breeding' in the south. The Mannings attended college, had a preacher in the family, my granddaddy built the school and helped start the church building.

"I wanted Gaylord to attend my Freshman Home-

80

coming dance at Duke. He had no transportation and had no money to rent a tuxedo. Gaylord has fierce pride and resented anybody giving him any handouts. So Daddy, knowing the situation, visited the Perrys one day. He asked, 'Gaylord, would you mind driving my car to Duke? I can't get away and Blanche desperately needs some clothes and books she left behind.' Gaylord happily agreed and timed his drive to Duke with the Homecoming Dance. But he refused any spending money, slept the night in the back seat of Daddy's car and drove home the next day.

"The economic difference in our families made it difficult for us because Gaylord was so conscious of it. I respected him for it, but pleaded with him that it didn't matter. There was no threat of my losing interest in Gaylord because of the college boys. They seemed so frivolous and immature while Gaylord seemed so serious and grown up, even in high school. But the truth is, if Gaylord hadn't got that big bonus to play baseball, he might never have overcome his 'hang-up' over the differences in our lifestyles and his relative poverty."

During the school year, when I wasn't involved in football, basketball or baseball, I looked for other diversions that would reduce my time in the classroom. I teamed up with Shelton Chesson, Larry Woolard and Dale Rodgerson, and we were all members of the school's livestock judging team. We'd travel all over the county competing with teams from other schools. It was, in a way, like scoring diving events. A qualified judge studied a steer, for instance, and came up with a point total based on the animal's body structure, the contour of the rump and chest, breeding, coat of fur, carriage in movement and the likelihood that the animal would pass on his traits to his offspring. Then our student scores were matched against the expert judge's. The closest was the winner.

I guess I wasn't too different from most boys. Life,

then, was having a good time when I wasn't playing sports. I always considered any grade higher than "C" an indication I was spending too much time on the course. I don't recall ever flunking any subject. I do recall stressing to my folks, however, that high grades don't mean a thing. It's how much you learn, I told them.

I did some acting at school, too. My great moment came in my junior year. There were only boys in my home room, and P.C. Bryant was the teacher in charge. We all discussed what kind of spring play we could put on for the school. P.C. Bryant remembers it: "Gaylord came up with this idea of a womanless wedding. Gaylord was about six-foot-three, and we had one boy about five-two. Naturally, Gaylord played the bride. And this tiny boy was the groom. We conducted the entire ceremony as if it were the real thing. Gaylord had high heels, a wig, wedding gown and veil and a bouquet. The groom was all decked out in his formal tuxedo. At the close of the ceremony, Gaylord picked up this boy, tucked him under his arm and carried him down the aisle. It was the funniest thing to happen in the school in a long while."

Our lives were full. There was little time and little pocket money to allow boys to gather under lamp posts on street corners and tempt mischief. There never was any trouble that needed the sheriff. Our town was too small to have fighting enemies. We were happy to see people. Williamston High holds nothing but warm memories for me. I played basketball for fun, just like football, and it was an excellent conditioner for baseball. (I took my baseball dead serious from the start.)

In my four seasons of basketball at Williamston, we won 94 of 102 games. I averaged close to 30 points, mainly with a one-hand jump shot, and more than 20 rebounds a game. This was enough to bring me about 20 basketball scholarship offers, some from big colleges across the country. But more important than anything else, basketball brought Blanche and me together.

Coach Thrift still remembers my basketball career vividly. "Gaylord was an eater," he says. "Belk Tyler, a local department store, gave the basketball team a banquet at the country club at the end of Jim's last year with Williamston. They served barbecue chicken. Jim and I kept count on Gaylord. He ate two whole chickens, two huge dishes of sweet potatoes and corn, eighteen rolls, a pecan pie, a quart of milk and a half dozen glasses of iced tea. And he didn't even take the time to unfold his napkin."

7

When the baseball season began during my freshman year at Williamston High, I had no desire to be a big pitching star. I just wanted to be the starting third baseman for the Williamston Green Wave.

Jim *was* the Williamston pitching staff his junior year. He had a 10–1 record the previous two seasons, and he'd walked only one batter his whole sophomore year. We played Tuesdays and Fridays, and Jim could handle two starts a week without much trouble.

But when the playoffs began, Williamston found itself faced with three games in one week. Jim couldn't pitch them all. Gaither Cline, our baseball coach that year, called over to me at third base where I was taking infield practice. "Gaylord," he said, "how'd you like to pitch tomorrow against Beargrass?"

"I don't mind if you don't mind," I said. "But you have to know, Coach, I never pitched in a regular game before."

"Gaylord, pitching's in your blood. Your daddy is one of the best in these parts still. We all know how good Jim is. I believe you can do it. No infielder in the conference has an arm like yours. And besides, we'll have Jim ready to spell you if you get into trouble."

That night at home, Daddy and Jim showed me everything I'd need: how to pitch off the rubber, take a stretch, hold runners on base. It was like cramming for an exam.

Before the game Gaither told me, "Be relaxed, Gaylord. Remember, those Beargrass boys have never faced you before. They won't know what to expect."

"That will make it even then, Coach, because I don't know what to expect either," I said. My game plan was simple: just wind up and let her go for the middle of the strike zone.

I remember the first two batters went out and I thought to myself, "What's so hard about this? I'll just shoot the ball a little lower and then experiment with some fancy stuff." I walked the next three batters on twelve pitches. The coach ran out to the mound. "Gaylord," he said, "I'm not giving up on the Perrys. No, sir. A Perry started this game, and a Perry will finish it. But I'm gonna call on Jim to help you out."

Jim, who was playing third base, trotted to the mound, and I went to third. It took Jim three pitches to strike out the next Beargrass batter and end the inning. We had a good hitting team—Jim and I both batted over .400—and we took a quick eight-run lead. I went back to the mound the next inning a little wiser. But I loaded the bases in the fifth and again in the seventh. Jim and I exchanged positions each time, and each time he got them out. I got my first pitching victory.

I became a pitcher at the age of sixteen, and I may

be a little prejudiced, but I think that's about the right age. I think a youngster's a lot better off if, until then, he plays some other position, so that he can play every day. That way, he learns all about the game—fielding, running, hitting. He learns to think like a hitter, which helps later when he has to think like a pitcher.

Another reason for delaying a youngster's start on the mound is the chance of arm injury. Doctors have told me that boys starting out at the age of nine or so and practicing their pitching through their growing years can do harm to the growth centers of the bone. That's certainly not worth the risk. The ability to become a major-league pitcher is more a gift of the Lord than anything else. An arm that can throw a baseball 80 to 90 miles an hour or more doesn't get it from an early start at the age of five. The middle teens is plenty early enough, and may add a few seasons during the peak earning years of a professional career.

After being scouted as thoroughly as Jim and I were, I know that scouts look mainly for strong, live arms that can throw fast balls that "move." The rest can be taught. Many young pitchers have asked me what kind of exercise is best to develop a body for pitching. I'd have to say pulling tobacco, wouldn't I?

I threw almost nothing but fast balls my freshman year. Daddy showed me the curve (and even the knuckle ball), but he wouldn't let me throw it often because he was concerned about me hurting my arm. "Just let them see it once in a while, Gaylord," he advised. "Putting the knowledge in the batter's head that you got it is as good as having the pitch itself." (That advice held up well later, with a different pitch.)

A lot was in the papers early that spring of 1955 about a pitch called a "spitter." The *Sporting News* polled 120 big-league coaches, managers and players, and 84 of them favored legalizing the spitter. The baseball commissioner, Ford Frick, said he'd like to see it back in baseball.

But the rules committee voted against legalizing it, six to three.

I didn't pay too much attention to the controversy. In those days, I figured my fast ball was good enough. Still, I asked Coach Gaither about the spitter.

"Gaylord, that's a grown man's pitch, nothing for a little old farm boy to mess with," Gaither said.

"Well, what does spit make the ball do?"

"I don't rightly know. But I know nobody on Williamston will throw it. Get it?"

"Just asking, Coach," I said.

"Well, all I know for sure is that it comes to the plate and does something nobody expects it to. Forget about it. We're having enough trouble coming up with a boy to catch you now. And what boy would want to catch a ball somebody spit all over? It'd be like taking another boy's chewing gum out of his mouth and chewing it yourself."

My freshman year, during the last five games on the way to the state finals, I won two shutouts and Jim won three. We gave up only 12 hits between us, and no man got as far as third base. In the finals, we played Colfax, best two-out-of-three, and they figured Jim would be tougher to beat than me, so they held back their ace, Bobby Simmons, till the second game. Jim won the first game, 9–0, on a two-hitter, and I came back to beat Bobby Simmons, 2–0, on a three-hitter. Neither Jim nor I made the all-state team picked by the Greensboro Daily News. Bobby Simmons did. Jim was 13–1 that season with five one-hitters. He allowed only one run all year and only 16 hits. I was 3–0 in the playoffs, and we both batted around .400.

I may have been a latecomer to pitching but once I got started, I sure took it seriously. I always wore a sweatshirt and a windbreaker, even on the hottest day. The other guys on the team would fight for a window seat in the cars we'd drive to the games, but not me. I wanted the middle, away from the draft.

I'll bet I had the best trainer in the state. Her name was Ruby Perry, my mamma. Day before I pitched, I'd sit down in the kitchen and she'd get out the bottle of Absorbine-Junior and rub my arm until it turned rosy-red. Then she'd apply some towels that had been boiled in water on the woodstove. Absorbine and Mamma were all I needed to stay ready.

Jim and I were both pretty practical young men. We had a teammate named Larry Woolard who had a few dollars more than most of us. One year, Larry was playing third base, which he wasn't too good at, and he told Jim, "Don't let them hit the ball to me and and I'll buy you a milk shake and hamburger." Larry went three games without a chance. Another time, he told me, "If you'll pitch a no-hitter today, I'll let you use my car tonight and I'll pay for the gas." Naturally, I pitched a no-hitter.

Willie Hardeson was my first Williamston catcher, and he did just fine by me. But after he graduated, I ran into a string of catchers who had trouble holding my pitches. In one seven-inning game, I had a no-hitter and struck out 16 batters—six of them in one inning because the catcher had as much trouble with my pitches as the batters did.

It seemed that every other pitch I threw went through the catcher, but I've got to give him credit. He got so good at playing the rebound off the backstop that once in a while he could actually throw out a runner trying to move up—provided my pitch hit the right spot on the backstop. Sometimes the catcher was turning around waiting for the rebound even before my pitch got to the plate. I suggested that we add a new column to the boxscore: rebounds. We considered moving our center fielder in, letting him play behind the catcher.

I was a hot-tempered youngster and had no patience

for errors behind me. Once, when my shortstop kicked one, I turned to him and yelled, "How can you miss a ball like that?"

Our coach heard the whole thing from the bench and came running to the mound. He spun me around so quickly, the ball flew out of my hand. "Gaylord? Who do you think you are?"

"Did you see that, Coach? I. . ."

"Shut up. Any boy you know who wants to make an error on purpose? The gate swings both ways, Gaylord. You give up walks. You give up hits, too. How 'bout these boys behind you coming to the mound and telling you off every time? You either pitch and keep quiet or get outta here right now. When you're perfect and start pitching perfect games, then you can criticize your teammates!"

Well, I did pitch a perfect game my junior year, but the coach was right. I had four head coaches in my four years at Williamston, and I can say one thing for sure: they didn't know much about baseball but, the important thing is, they didn't pretend that they knew. I respected them for that.

Most of my coaching came from Dad—gently and quickly. If I gave up a bunch of hits, he would never criticize me about that game. But the next game I'd pitch, he'd remind me, "Gaylord, keep the ball down." It was always positive and never emotional. Or if I made an error at third base, he wouldn't say a thing. But he'd hit ground balls to me every night that week. We'd have contests to see how many I could catch without a miss. Dad's whole idea was, "Work and practice and you'll be all right." And as for rewarding us? Well, Jim and I considered playing high school baseball a privilege. I think that made us play harder.

Daddy says now, "All I did was give them a love for the game and a chance to play it," but, of course, he did a lot more.

After Williamston High won the state baseball title, Jim left for Campbell College. The coach my sophomore year, Thurston Callihan, said, "Gaylord, you're our number one pitcher because you did so well last year and because we don't have anybody else in the school who can pitch." Guess that wasn't the greatest vote of confidence, but I was hooked on pitching. That year, I was 12–2 with four no-hitters. But we didn't quite make it to the State finals.

I really blossomed in my junior year. I opened the season with a perfect game over the Ahoskie Indians, striking out 14 of the 21 men I faced. That year I won 14, lost one and pitched five no-hitters. I averaged better than two strike-outs an inning and didn't allow an earned run the whole season.

The Greenboro *Telegram* had some nice words for me just before the state finals against Kernersville: "If Gaylord Perry were old enough to run for mayor of Williamston, he'd probably win the election in a shutout. . . . On the mound, he becomes a fluid-motion spring of pitching power, concentrating intently on every pitch. Big hands with long, strong fingers and a whiplike arm make his fast ball blaze with an authority that simply masters a hitter."

Kernersville must've forgot to read my clippings. They beat me and beat us out of the state title. Funny thing is, the week before, I no-hit Oak City in the district playoffs. The morning of that game, I took sick at school and was sent to the hospital with a 102-degree fever. Our family doctor, Dr. Brown, let me go home on the promise I'd go right to bed. Well, I lived up to my promise, but first I took a detour to school to catch my final classes. "The hospital said I was well enough to come to class, and if I can come to class, I can pitch," I told Coach Maness. I struck out 14, walked two in a 12–0 victory. Then I went home to bed just like Doc Brown ordered. Mamma and Daddy didn't cotton to illness. A farm family doesn't have patience for it. We had to be too sick to move to stay home from school, or to miss a game. That discipline's helped me in the big leagues. Going into the 1974 season, I haven't missed a starting assignment since May of 1966 when I dislocated my ankle on a slide.

All through high school—and ever since—I've been blessed with one of the best rooters anyone could hope for. Her name is Mattie Coletrain, and she lives in a big old farmhouse. She's known me since I was a barefoot boy, but she's never laid eyes on me. She's blind. But she sure has laid her heart on me. I've been visiting with her and talking about sports with her since high school. She is my greatest fan next to Blanche and our folks.

Mattie can't get around too well, but she follows me across the country on her radios—four of them. She has listened to my games from as far west as Houston and as far north as Boston. She has a phone right by her bed and the moment the game ends, she calls Daddy and fills him in. Mattie's a regular scouting service.

I use a radio myself to scout the opposition. It's a short-wave tuner that can pick up ball games all over the country. I carry it with me everywhere I go. It's amazing how much information a broadcaster gives out during his play-by-play. I've learned about pitches that are troubling certain hitters, injuries that might affect a man's swing, pitches a man's been hitting well, all kinds of little tidbits. Of all the baseball broadcasters, I've found Ernie Harwell of Detroit and Harry Caray of Chicago the most informative. I hope their regular listeners appreciate them as much as I do.

Just before the end of my junior year in Williamston High I got a letter from Herb Kokernot, Jr., a rich Texan who sponsored a semipro team in Alpine, Texas. A Milwaukee scout named Sam Allen had recommended me highly even though Alpine was a team made up of top college prospects and I was only in high school. My folks were impressed with the offer which would provide first-rate competition, excellent playing facilities and air travel to games throughout Colorado, New Mexico and Texas. The coach was Tom Chandler, the baseball coach at Texas A.&M. The pay was $400 a month for shooting rabbits on Mr. Kokernot's farm and serving meals at his Baptist Church; you played baseball for nothing like a good amateur. The boys got use of a car and bunked at Sul Ross College in Alpine.

It all sounded good except Daddy needed me on the farm. Jim was pitching in the Northern League that summer. That left Daddy and Annox. Besides, Daddy had rented some extra land for me to work so I could earn a little extra spending money that summer. Daddy would be stuck with all the land to work.

Daddy had always sacrificed and worked extra hard so that Jim and I could play sports. He would do our work rather than ask us to give up a game. But sending me to Alpine was a big step, and Daddy had to think about it carefully. He wasn't only worried about losing a farm-hand. He was worried about me being on my own for the first time. Finally, he went down to Alpine with me—Mr. Kokernot paid the way for both of us—checked out the set-up and liked what he saw. The fact that I was going to turn over $300 of my $400 a month to pay for farm help made Daddy's decision a little easier.

Alpine matured me as a pitcher and as a person. Playing six games a week and learning from Mr. Chandler and the college boys gave me polish. I learned to throw a curve ball and a change-of-pace and added a side-arm delivery. And I learned how to fly in an airplane. We had one of those little old DC-3's, and I got pretty airsick a few times. I got over homesickness easily. Every time I thought about Mom and Dad, I remembered all the back-breaking work I was missing in the fields and I felt "just fine. . . in Alpine."

My brother Jim had a 15–12 record and a 2.88 earned-run-average in his second pro season. He won the attention of Cleveland's roving pitching coach, Red Ruffing, when he struck out 16 batters one game.

That same summer, the spitter was in the sports pages again. Lew Burdette of Milwaukee defeated the Cincinnati Reds, 1–0, the first week of the season, and the Reds' manager, Birdie Tebbetts, filed a protest, accusing Burdette of throwing the illegal pitch. The Cincinnati general manager, Gabe Paul, photographed Burdette, trying for incriminating evidence. "Nobody found nothing," they said. At about the same time, Mickey Owen, managing at Jacksonville, came up with the statement that a dozen big-league pitchers were using Vaseline on the ball. I couldn't imagine what for.

Four women helped persuade me to sign a professional baseball contract upon my graduation from Williamston. Their names were Connie, Diane, Flossie and Audrey. They were not nice women. They were four hurricanes and they did terrible things to the crops in North Carolina between 1955 and 1957. The fourth lady, Audrey, caught our tobacco, peanuts and corn just short of maturity and completely leveled them. She left Mamma and Daddy more in debt than ever before. Audrey pushed aside any thoughts I had of taking a combined basketball-and-baseball scholarship to one of the several large northern universities that were after me.

Jim was hard-pressed to help out the folks because he was on meager minor-league pay and trying to finish his education at Campbell College in the off-season. Daddy took to carpentry and other labor in Williamston, but there was little work with so many tenant farmers wiped out by the storms. It was up to me to do something, and the only thing I could do was get a big bonus to play pro baseball.

To tell the truth, I'm not sure how much the scouts were impressed by my fast ball and how much by Mom's blackberry pie. My senior year was full of friendly scouts who found their way into the kitchen as graduation day approached. There were scouts from most all the big-league clubs every day I went to the mound. It was a lot of pressure on a tobacco farmer and his son who together had only one thought: how much we can get to sign?

Mrs. Perry didn't bring no fool into the world. I wasn't going to throw out my arm or get a hitch in my shoulder at that stage of the bonus game. My caution may have cost me some money. It was an unusually wet chilly spring. Daddy and I talked it over and decided I wasn't going to start letting out my arm until the weather warmed and I could get loose. As a result, I didn't have as good a spring with Williamston as I had had the previous three seasons. In fact I wound up with only a 7–2 record and only one one-hitter.

Somehow, the rumor got going that I had hurt my arm. A New York Giants' scout named Earl Smith heard the rumors, and he knew better. He had seen Jim and me pitch since we began at Williamston. He had been touting the Giants on me since the state championship game in my freshman year. Earl knew I wasn't cutting loose, but, of course, he didn't tell the opposing scouts. He figured why should he build up the competition—and drive up the price?

Still, the scouts hung around the farm. They'd come by the fields where Daddy was working the crops and strike up casual conversations with him.

"Evan Perry?"

"That's me."

"I've been scouting Gaylord. He's a fine boy."

"Yep."

"Have one of these Havana see-gars."

"I'll take one for Annox."

"You can have the whole box. It's back in the car. How's Gaylord?"

"Nothing wrong with him, I know. Seen him this morning. . . . Excuse me, sir, but you're standing on

94

those tobacco seedlings I'm gonna have to plant sometime."

"Gosh, I'm sorry, Mr. Perry. Say, how'd you like a drive up to Edenton for Gaylord's next game?"

"That'd be fine. Right fine."

The scouts spent a lot of time with Mamma in the kitchen, too. The scouts were devouring barbecue chicken and blueberry pies like they were going out of style. Daddy told me, "Gaylord, you better hurry up and sign before these scouts eat us out of house and home." I think some of the scouts wanted to make a package deal for mother and son.

On Graduation Day, I had to endure a few disappointments. First, I lost out to my buddy, Shelton Chesson, as outstanding athlete of our class. I won eleven varsity letters, but I'd quit football in my senior year. Shelton starred in three sports and deserved the honor. Next, I lost out on "Student Who Contributed Most to School and Community" because one of my teachers said I hadn't paid my 25-cent class dues. And, thirdly, no scouts came around waving $100,000 offers.

They hadn't exactly forgotten me. There were a dozen or so scouts at graduation, sitting in the last row of seats loaned by the Biggs Funeral Home. The trouble was that unimpressive senior year of mine. I had to show the scouts I was better than my record. George Griffin, the man I dried dishes for, hit on the idea of a special game at Smithfield, N.C.—me against a team of selected semi-pro stars. After watching me for four seasons at Williamston High, scouts could use this game as a final yardstick to measure my value—in bonus dollars. It put a lot of pressure on me.

The weather turned chilly the night of the big game. It was a good crowd, about 1,000 people. Mom and Daddy were there, and Blanche and her daddy and all of Farm Life that could get there. The opposing pitcher was Tommy Byrne, the former big-leaguer.

I can't say I was as relaxed as I would have been fishing at Mill Pond. I figured there might be $80,000 riding on this one ball game. Not bad stakes for a boy who once got $25, two chickens and a side of bacon for winning a semipro game in Farm Life.

I walked the first three batters I faced. The scouts started buzzing. They figured they were about to save themselves a heap of money.

I called time and started kicking at the mound. Then I sent someone to the tool barn for a hammer and a rake. The pitching "rubber" was made of wood, and it had come loose. I got down with the hammer and started pounding fresh twenty-penny nails into the buried piece of board that held the "rubber." Then I smoothed the dirt with a rake. It took me about ten minutes.

One fan yelled, "Hey, Gaylord, are you auditioning for a big-league grounds crew?"

Another hollered, "Perry, it's too late to be puttin' you tee-bac-kee in now." Everybody had himself a good laugh.

I took five warmups and then struck out the next 17 batters in a row—all college stars or former professional players.

Tom Sheehan, the head scout for the Giants, wrote down something on a piece of paper and handed it to Tim Murchison, his head man. Then Sheehan jumped in a car and drove to Raleigh where he caught a plane for New York.

I won the game 5–1, striking out more than 20 batters.

Then the auction began in earnest. Tim Murchison later told me what Sheehan's note had said: "Tim. . . start at $50,000. . . then go up $10,000 to $15,000 more. . . don't stop bidding. . . call the office if it takes more money. . . That boy's gonna be a good one—Tom." All the scouts hightailed it back to Williamston to prepare their bids. They piled into Griffin's Quick Lunch for some psychological warfare, and my friend George Griffin eavesdropped a little.

"I don't know," said one. "I don't think Gaylord's that quick."

"I could call his breaking pitch most every time," added another.

"You know he's older than most high school boys at graduation," said another.

"Looks to me like he's got a tendency to put on weight."

"That motion will get him into arm trouble unless he's careful."

"You can't tell about a kid until you know what kind of heart he has."

"Wonder if he'd look as fast in the daylight. Those Smithfield lights weren't too good."

It was going on 3 A.M. and George Griffin's feet were about to give out. He walked over to the scouts, all running me down to scare out the opposition, and he said, "Boys, I've known Gaylord since he was a small boy. And you've overlooked some real flaws in him. He sucked his thumb until he was nine, he's losing his hair already and he doesn't drink or smoke."

Those scouts were a good old bunch, but some of them were really out of place down on the farm. Our mule, Mollie, bit the finger of one scout trying to feed her sugar. (We were looking for sugar for me, not Mollie.) Another sat down on a pile of mule manure and we never saw him again. Our dogs chased one scout who showed up after dark. They're persistent people; I heard about one scout who, to sign a prospect, got engaged to his spinster sister; they say she would have scared a hog.

The most exciting thing I remember about tobacco

growing was visiting the warehouses. It was just like those old Lucky Strike cigarette commercials: "Fifty-five-five-five-five, fifty-six-six-six-six-six-six, fifty-seven-seven-seven-seven-seven-seven, fifty-eight-eight-eight-eight-eight, SOLD AMERICAN!"

That was what my negotiations with the scouts were like. Daddy knew we had prime goods, and he'd set a base price of $40,000. There were other considerations besides money, but I can't remember them.

My brother Jim kept in telephone contact with us. (He was at Reading, Pennsylvania, where he wound up with a 16–8 record, a 2.79 earned run average and an invitation to Cleveland's spring training camp the next year.) "Give each club a fair chance," Jim advised. "Take every promise that isn't in writing with a grain of salt. Go with the club which offers you the most money, but consider the quality of the organization, the pitching needs of the big club and how fast they bring along their prospects.

Most of the clubs dropped out early in the bidding, the Cleveland Indians among them. I thought they would come up with a good offer because they had Jim. But they didn't. Jim hadn't been pitching real well yet and maybe one Perry was all the organization could handle at the time. But to tell the truth, if the Indians had come only close to the others, I would have signed with them just to be with Jim. I think the Indians' best offer was about $7,000. I believe the Indians thought that Jim would sway me into signing with them and that they could get me cheap. Jim told me *not* to be influenced by the fact that he was with Cleveland. Washington came up with a real good offer, not a big bonus but a promise to put me right into the big leagues. The Yankee offer was low. They tried to sell me on the greatness of the Yankee uniform and annual pennant shares. I wanted something substantial.

Finally, four clubs were left—Baltimore, Philadelphia, Milwaukee and the Giants. The Orioles had given a $125,000 bonus to an outfielder named Dave Nicholson, so when the bidding reached $60,000 they dropped out. The Phillies insisted on a workout in Philadelphia first. That took it down to two.

Milwaukee decided to invest $100,000 in Tony Cloninger who was also a high-school senior in North Carolina that year. The Giants were surprised. They'd expected to get Cloninger. They didn't want to lose me, too.

The negotiations at my house lasted two days, and after overhearing a few other bids and sampling a lot of Mamma's cooking, the Giants made the bid we wanted: a bonus plus three years of salary, all adding up to $73,500 —the most the Giants had ever paid a rookie.

I called Blanche and told her the news. She had news, too. She was crowned Miss Daniel Johnson Raceway queen. Then I got Daddy and Mamma together and told them that I was going to give them $35,000 of my bonus. The rest I banked. Daddy taught me to earn what I get paid for. The same applied to them. They earned half my bonus with their sacrifices for me, and I really enjoyed giving it to them.

Daddy got all choked up. For the first time in his life, he was going to be out of debt—all because he encouraged his sons to play ball. He turned away from me and his eyes watered up and he blew his nose. It sounded like a boat whistle on the Roanoke River, and we all had a good laugh.

8

While the Giants tried to figure out whether to assign me to Fresno of the California League or St. Cloud of the Northern League, both Class C teams, I spent a few days pitching batting practice at Phoenix, the Giants' Triple-A team. Phoenix had several future big-leaguers in its lineup —including Leon Wagner, Felipo Alou, Tom Haller and Willie McCovey—most of whom kept riding me about my big bonus. When the word came through I was going to St. Cloud, Minnesota, Leon Wagner offered me some advice. "Don't worry about a thing," said Daddy Wags. "You'll do real fine up on St. Cloud Nine. And if you don't, you just buy the club."

I reported to St. Cloud in the middle of a ball game. I went straight to the locker room, pulled on my first pro uniform and checked myself out in a clouded mirror cracked at the bottom. (I later learned somebody had thrown a bat at it.) I stood on a stool to check my pants, then tilted my cap to give me an "I've-been-around" look. And out I went to start my career. Just as I reached the dugout, so did the plate umpire. The bench had been riding him good. He had reached his kindling point.

"Get the hell outta here," he roared. "All of you. Everyone. Out!"

"Me too?" I asked. "I just got here."

"Son," the umpire bellowed. "I didn't tell you to put on that suit, but I sure can tell you to take it off. Get outta here!"

That was my introduction to professional baseball. Only nine men were allowed to remain on the bench, along with our manager, Richie Klaus. The rest of us had to spend the game back in the locker room.

It was an interesting season, and a good one from my point of view. I had some pretty talented teammates—Matty Alou and Bob Bolin among them—and some pretty talented opponents. My first pro game, I beat Winnipeg, 4–2. The losing pitcher was Ray Sadecki, later my teammate on the Giants.

Aberdeen, managed by Earl Weaver, had three pretty fair pitchers—Steve Barber, Bo Belinsky and a fellow you may never have heard of, Steve Dalkowski. We took the league title by winning 19 of our last 21 games, and three days before the end of the season, I went 17 innings and beat Steve Barber. The Giants were furious when they heard; they didn't want a kid they'd paid $70,000 burned out at the age of nineteen. Actually, it was my idea, not the manager's. I finished the season 9–5 and finished second to Belinsky with a 2.39 ERA. Belinsky also led the league in strike-outs and women.

Let me tell you about Dalkowski. He was the fastest and wildest pitcher I ever saw. In 62 innings at Aberdeen that year, he struck out 121. And he walked 112. Bob

Bolin and I had a running bet: either of us would buy the other a steak if he fouled off one of Dalkowski's blue darters. Neither of us ever collected. When I first saw Dalkowski throw, I thought to myself, "If he can throw that hard and not be in the big leagues, how will I ever make it?" Dalkowski never did make it to the majors, but a lot of people still insist he was the fastest pitcher who ever lived—and the wildest.

I discovered two things quick in pro ball. First, the guys who were being paid to hit were much better hitters than I'd ever faced, and, second, it was a good thing I *wasn't* being paid to hit. Despite my .400 lifetime batting average for the Williamston Green Wave, I'd have starved to death with my bat as a pro. I had a total of five singles in my rookie year.

At St. Cloud, we traveled to games in a caravan of four station wagons, taking turns driving. We got $2.50 a day for food—mostly hamburgers—and on the road, we lived barracks style, crowding as many as ten guys in a room. One of the guys who'd been around said we had a great club because nobody snored.

Bob Bolin and I shared an upstairs flat in St. Cloud. We ate at the Press Bar since they gave ballplayers 20 percent off on meals. When I joined the club, the local paper gave me a writeup, mostly about my big bonus. I guess people expected me to arrive in a Cadillac convertible and wearing flashy clothes. My style always has been Ford and Chevy, suits off the rack, shirts from the counter and my meat well-done. Bolin had a car, and I helped buy the gas. I saved money for both of us by catching fish in the Mississippi River, and I saved money for myself by never smoking or drinking (still don't).

Bolin and I were a perfect match, a pair of farm boys. We hit it off right from the first day—when he bet me a steak I couldn't run 100 laps around the park. I nearly died doing it, but I did it. Bolin thought I was a terrific competitor, but the truth is I'm a terrific eater. I really wanted the steak.

I went back to the farm after that season, and the first payment on my bonus arrived on the 15th of September. The bonus was spread over three years, and the check was for $20,000—$10,000 for me and $10,000 for Daddy. He was just about $10,000 in debt and it was a great day when we wiped out all those debts that had gnawed at him for some twenty years. (The next year, Daddy opened a bank account for the first time in his life.)

I bought a brand-new Plymouth I needed to start classes at Campbell Junior College. Mamma bought a new bed to replace the one they'd had since they got married, a new oil heater, an oil stove to replace the wood-burning model, new curtains and a rug. Mamma also bought two dresses and a new hat for herself. She was careful what she bought. She didn't want the neighbors thinking she was putting on the dog.

The biggest thing for Daddy was peace of mind. He was really hurt when government tax men said, "Evan, that bonus is none of your own money. It's Gaylord's and he must pay the taxes on the full bonus."

Three years later, in 1961, the government hit me with $17,500 in penalties on my $60,000 bonus. Daddy and I had paid separate income tax on the bonus we'd split. We argued that he had acted as my agent and had suffered expenses that justified his getting half the bonus. We hired a lawyer who advised us to pay and then to sue the government for return of the money. By 1961, I'd bought Daddy a farm; I was earning only $3,600 baseball salary, and I couldn't pay off the government demand. I went to the owner of the Giants, Horace Stoneham, and explained the problem. He wrote out a check interest-free for $17,500 without batting an eye. I didn't repay him until the court settlement was reached four years later when the Government returned $16,000 to me.

103

The reason I bring this up is that my case set a precedent for bonus-sharing with parents. The Perry settlement later affected decisions for Richie Allen, Randy Hundley and Dick Dietz. I'll be forever grateful to Mr. Stoneham for his kindness to me while I was struggling away in the minors.

But Mr. Stoneham's kindness had limits. My first day at Campbell College, I was walking from my dormitory to the gymnasium, with my gym shoes tied together and hanging over my shoulder. Right in front of the gym, I spotted Earl Smith and Tim Murchison, the two Giant scouts. I hadn't seen them since I left to play ball at St. Cloud.

"Hey, where you going?" called Tim.

"I'm going to basketball practice."

"Oh no, you're not," said Earl.

"What do you mean? I got a scholarship here—to play basketball."

"No," said Tim. "The Giants called and told us to be sitting here waiting on you. Not to let you play basketball."

The Giants never did let me play basketball. That cost me my scholarship, but I really can't complain. It gave me a lot more time to visit Blanche at Duke University.

My second minor-league season was spent in Corpus Christi, Texas, and one night about eleven o'clock, right after a night game, we left Corpus in a bus, aiming to arrive in Tulsa, 450 miles away, sometime early the next afternoon. To save travel expenses, the club tried to time its arrivals after the noon check-in times at the hotels.

This one particular trip, I was going to start the next game, so I got the whole back seat to stretch out on during the trip. After a few bumpy hours, I dozed off. Suddenly, I was awakened, believing I had died and come back to life as a chicken.

Somewhere along the route in the black of night, our trainer-driver had dozed at the wheel. The bus had gone off the road, barely missed a farmhouse, picked up three lines of wash, plowed through a hay barn and smashed to a stop in the henhouse, scattering squawking birds everywhere. From that day on, our trainer, Harry Jordan, heard "Boo-awk, bawk-bawk-bawk" instead of hello from us players. (Incidentally, we bought the chickens we hit and ate them when we got to Tulsa. That turned out to be the most thrilling moment in my minor-league career.)

At Corpus Christi, I had my own locker for the first time; my knee-length white sanitary socks got washed every day; meal money went up to $4.50 a day; the last man in the shower didn't have to worry about the warm water giving out; I didn't have to rub my own arm with Absorbine-Junior; there were two speeds on the electric fan in the clubhouse; and the fly paper got changed three times a week. Still, what I remember best about Corpus Christi—beyond the oil refineries, beyond the heat, beyond everything—are the bus rides, through chickens and, even worse, through Mexico.

The Texas League had an agreement to play a number of games in Mexico City, Monterrey, Veracruz, Nueva Larado and Poza Rica. Our Mexican driver picked us up at the border and took us through treacherous mountain roads to the ball parks. We rode ten-year-old second-hand buses with tires as smooth as the top of my head and brakes that squealed. Our driver, "Laughing Lopez" we called him, used to go around the mountain corners at 35 or 40 miles an hour, laughing and blowing his horn as if that would clear the road by itself. I don't want to remember how many times we side-swiped buses going the opposite direction and ripped off our side view mirror.

The back seat of the bus was reserved for a spare tire, extra water and oil and a first-aid kit containing two bottles of tequila and a bottle of something called "pulque." Lopez said he used the pulque to fix flat tires. He did. He drank it while fixing the flats.

105

When we survived the bus ride we still had the water, the fans and the rumors of bandits to contend with. Mexico really made me yearn for the big leagues—or even for Williamston. At least I could handle the water at home. I didn't have too good a year at Corpus Christi. I was 10–11 with a 4.05 earned run average, and our club finished dead last.

To ease my miseries of losing, a bunch of my teammates took me out one night "to relax." I'd never tasted liquor and they took me into this Texas honky-tonk bar and bought me some sweet-tasting spirits. There were painted women there, the kind you see in magazines in the barbershop. I proceeded to get higher than a kite. When I returned to earth the next morning, I vowed I'd never touch hard liquor again. I'll sip wine now, but that's as far as I'll go.

Life took a happy turn that fall when I proposed to Blanche on Halloween night. We married the day after Christmas.

Another good thing happened in 1959. My brother Jim made it to the big leagues, a big jump up from the Eastern League and only two years after he was pitching in the Northern League.

In 1959, Cleveland was a pennant contender—for the last time in recent history—and Jim posted a 12–10 record and a 2.65 earned run average, the best ERA among Indian pitchers.

In 1960 I went back to Double-A in the Texas League; the Giants had moved the team from Corpus to Harlington, Texas, and changed its name to the Rio Grande Valley. We changed our style, too. We jumped from last place to first, and I led the league with an earned run average of 2.83. I also led the league in defeats; I was 9–13. I wasn't too happy because that was the final year I was getting paid $5,000—under my bonus contract—and I figured I'd be taking a cut in 1961. I figured right.

Three Texas teammates—Bobby Bolin, Ron Herbel and Dick LeMay, all pitchers—were called up to the Giants, which didn't help my morale any. Much worse, during the team's second trip into Mexico, Blanche suffered a miscarriage. I didn't even know she'd been in the hospital till I returned from Mexico.

"Gaylord," Ray Murray, my manager, said one day, "the sooner you learn the overall strategy of the game, the sooner you'll reach your full potential as a pitcher. You've got to learn to field and hit as well as pitch."

"Well, if I have to wait to learn to hit until I can pitch in the big leagues, I may not live long enough," I said. I had a grand total of 22 hits in three seasons of pro ball.

"I'm not telling you that you have to hit. I'm telling you you have to learn how to hit, the thinking behind it. That way, you'll learn what the hitter is thinking which will make you a better pitcher."

Slowly, I began to realize that my raw talent alone would not make me a big-league winning pitcher. I'd have to learn all the theories—and all the tricks.

Ray Murray always had a way of sneaking some humor into my serious world. "We're playing at Austin tomorrow," he said one day, "and there's gonna be a guy warming up before the game whose style reminds me a lot of yours. Watch him. Maybe it'll help you."

"What's his name?" I said.

"Max Patkin," Murray said.

"Thanks, Ray. I never heard of him, but I'll watch him."

Max Patkin turned out to be a former minor-league pitcher who turned clown to entertain fans at ball parks all over the country. His cap turned sideways, Patkin's loose-boned body gave him the look of something I remember seeing stuck on a broomstick in a corn field down home. I roared when I saw the guy I was to copy.

While I was losing games in Texas, the Giants were losing in the big leagues. They sank all the way to fifth place, and I could tell from reading the papers they needed pitching help. I could also tell from the papers that my brother was having another big year. Jim was 18–10 for Cleveland in 1960; he also got married that year, to Daphne Kay Snell, a North Carolina girl.

My career wasn't coming along quite so brightly. The Giants cut me to $3,600 a year. But there were three consolations: first, I got into a National Guard unit so I didn't have to go on active duty in the army; second, $3,600 was still as much as Daddy earned for a year of tobacco; and, third, the Giants were promoting me to Tacoma in the Triple-A Pacific Coast League, just one step short of the big leagues.

At Tacoma, somebody cleaned and shined my baseball shoes after every game, meal money went up to $7.50 and all the travel was by airplane. Tacoma had a few ex-Giants such as knuckle-ball pitcher Eddie Fisher, catcher Tom Haller, and the hero of the 1954 World Series, Dusty Rhodes—guys who were used to living the big-league life. Some sponsor gave a slab of steak for each pitching victory. I won 16 steaks and lost ten. I was third in the league with a 2.55 earned run average, which put me ahead of both Satchell Paige, who was pitching for Portland at the age of about sixty, and Sam McDowell, who was pitching for Salt Lake City at the age of nineteen. Paige had an ERA of 2.88, a lot better than McDowell's. Our club hated to face McDowell. He was so wild, and his ball was so live that Tommy Haller used to say, "I want a stethoscope put on it to count its pulse."

That season, Vancouver manager Jack McKeon experimented with tiny radio receivers in the hats of his pitchers. McKeon could call the pitches, even remind the pitcher of the outs, the batter's average and the game situation. Vancouver pitcher Art Bamberger was on the mound when the cap radio was tried once. It went something like this, I think:

"Hello, Art?"

Bamberger nods.

"Art, this is Haller at bat."

Nod.

"Don't give him anything too good to hit. But don't walk him."

Nod.

Haller doubles.

"Okay, get him next time. Now here's Chuck Hiller. Throw him a curve."

Nod.

Base hit.

"Hello, Art? Runners on first and third and no outs. It's Dusty Rhodes. If he hits it to you, double play, second to first. You're not following through enough. Come up over the top more. Don't forget to take your stretch. Now waste a fast ball away on him."

Six nods.

Rhodes clears the bases with a fast ball thrown down the middle.

End of experiment.

We won the pennant by ten games, and at the end of the season, the Giants placed me on their 40-man roster. The big leagues. I'd play there for nothing, I thought to myself. The Giants must have been reading my mind. With my big league promotion, the club boosted my pay $900 to a grand total of $4500. If I lasted in San Francisco for 30 days of the 1962 season, I'd get $5000; 60 days, $5500; and $7000 for a full year. Oh well, that was almost two years planting tobacco back home.

The Giants finished third in 1961, despite the fact that Orlando Cepeda hit 46 homers and drove in 142 runs, and Willie Mays had 40 home runs and a .308 batting average. The Giants won 85 games, but not a single starting pitcher won more than 13 games. A little pitching help—from me, I hoped—could mean a pennant in 1962.

As things brightened for me, Jim was struggling with a slipping Cleveland club. He had a 10–17 record.

109

That October, the general manager of the Chicago White Sox, Ed Short, drew headlines when he officially asked the rules committee to legalize the spitball. Commissioner Ford Frick said he would not oppose a move to legalize the pitch. Me? I didn't much care. I was just happy to get home to a good old-fashioned east Carolina hog-killing—a real special event—and to look ahead to putting on my first real big-league uniform.

. . . . . .

9

. . . . . .

I kicked hard at the rubber, several times. The rubber
didn't come loose, not the way it had at Smithfield four
years earlier, when I was auditioning for all those scouts.
This was October 2, 1962, and I was pitching for a lot
more than a bonus. I was trying to pitch the San Francisco Giants into the World Series.

The Dodgers and the Giants had finished in a tie for
first place, and we had won the first playoff game. Now
it was the bottom of the ninth inning of the second play-
off game, the score tied 7–7, Maury Wills on second, Jim
Gilliam on first, nobody out and Daryl Spencer coming to
bat. I was brought in to face Spencer.

Al Dark, our manager, came out to the mound. "Gaylord," he said, "the Dodgers will be bunting." Everybody
in the place knew that, even a raw rookie from North

111

Carolina. Dark told me that as soon as I started my delivery, third baseman Jim Davenport and first baseman Orlando Cepeda would charge toward the plate, and shortstop Jose Pagan would break for third base. My job was to throw a strike, a pitch that could be bunted. "If you field the ball," Dark told me, "go to third with your throw. Pagan'll be there ahead of Wills. Let's go."

Dark hadn't talked to me that much all year, not when I made the club in the spring, not when he sent me down to Tacoma in the summer, not when he brought me back up in September.

I took my stretch, looked to second where Pagan was faking Wills back toward the base, turned and threw. The bunt was a good one. I fielded it, turned to throw to third base and saw that Wills was even with Pagan in the race to the bag. I reacted immediately. I decided I couldn't possibly get Wills. I wheeled and fired to first base, getting Spencer, allowing Wills and Gilliam to move up.

Alvin Dark exploded. He tore a telephone off the dugout wall and threw it from one end of the dugout to the other. Then he really got mad. He ran out to the mound and didn't even look at me. He just yanked the ball out of my hand and pointed to the bullpen. He wanted Mike McCormick. He told Mike to walk Tommy Davis intentionally. The next batter hit a short fly ball, and Maury Wills—the runner I was supposed to cut down—raced home and gave the Dodgers an 8–7 victory.

Wills ended the game and I started my struggle to regain Dark's confidence. I never succeeded. Alvin didn't really speak to me again until two years later, when he was on his way out as manager. He liked to make instant judgments about people, and from that day on I was a loser in his eyes. In the locker room, after the defeat, he walked right past me without a word. I felt miserable. But then two people helped lift my depression. Mays came by and patted me on the shoulder sympathetically. And Larry

112

Jansen, the pitching coach, sat down with me and said, "Forget it, it's not the end of the world."

The next morning, in the paper, Alvin Dark was quoted as saying, "Perry had time, but he just kicked it, that's all. There can be no excuse. Wills was definitely out if the play had been made."

One San Francisco sportswriter called my move "a colossal blunder," and most of the press and most Giant fans agreed with him. I don't know what they would have done to me if we hadn't won the third playoff game and moved into the World Series against the Yankees.

I wasn't eligible for the Series because I had rejoined the club in September. Dark must have been grateful for that.

When I reported to the Giants' spring training camp in 1962, it really wasn't the first time I'd been there. I was there for one day in 1959, when they needed a body to pitch batting practice. Manager Bill Rigney called me over, and I decided I was really going to impress him. I know I impressed Willie Mays.

The first pitch I threw to Mays had everything on it but direction. It went toward his left ear, and Mays went sprawling into the dirt. Willie Kirkland and Leon Wagner, standing nearby, were laughing so hard they could hardly stand.

"Ease up, boy. Ease up. We're on the same club," yelled Mays.

I was dying of embarrassment. My next pitch nearly hit Wagner standing outside the batting cage. Mays laughed and Wagner disappeared into the dugout. When he returned, he had on catcher's equipment and had tied a towel to the end of his bat. He waved it at me. "I want to be sure you know *exactly* where I'm standing," yelled Wags.

Rigney called me over to the sidelines. "Son," he said,

"just relax. We didn't bring you over here to make the club. We just want some medium-speed strikes. You've got a great future with the Giants. Don't expect it all to come to you today."

"Yes sir, Mr. Rigney. Thanks."

He smiled, patted me on the back and handed me the ball. "Now go out there and throw the ball over." I dropped the ball he handed me, bent over to pick it up and hit my head on the cross-bar of the batting cage. The bar and my head made a funny "bonk" sound. I pretended I didn't feel a thing, but I had nearly knocked myself cold. Rig called after me, "Gaylord, don't worry about making an impression. We won't forget you for quite a while."

In 1962, I was a little more sophisticated. Not much, but a little. This time I made the right kind of impression. I beat out Ron Herbel and Dick LeMay for the tenth place on the pitching roster. I was going to be a spot starter, which I liked, and a reliever, which I didn't. I had seen too many guys sent down from the big leagues after ruining their arms in the bullpen.

No player ever forgets his first "opening day," his first strike-out or first victory. Each was a special moment for me because I had never seen a big-league ball park before. Here are my remembrances of those dates, plus a few others from my rookie year:

April 10: Juan Marichal blanked Milwaukee at Candlestick Park, 6–0, before 39,177 on opening day. It was quite a moment for me that first time, walking onto the field. I paused, I looked up at the crowd, took a deep breath of satisfaction and . . . my cap blew off in the wind.

April 14: My first pitching appearance was my first starting assignment. My stomach felt like a bagful of swirling feathers. Don Blasingame was my first big-league out on a popper to Chuck Hiller. Eddie Kasko grounded out to Pagan. Vada Pinson grounded out the same way. I had an earned run average of 0.00 after one big-league inning! When I left a few innings later, after getting Tommy Harper for my first strike-out, the score was 4–4, and my ERA had soared. I can't say I enjoyed my first big-league early shower too much.

April 25: Ed Bailey hit a two-run homer to give me my first victory, 5–2, over Pittsburgh. I pitched exactly five innings, the minimum required for an official victory. I faced two batters in the sixth inning, gave up two singles and discovered that Alvin Dark didn't believe in having rookies work their own way out of trouble.

I celebrated victory No. 1 with a Pepsi filled with salted peanuts and met Blanche outside after the game to whoop it up, which meant going home and having a steak dinner. I didn't much like Blanche coming to the games, but I'm glad she saw that one.

April 30: Homers by Mays and Cepeda helped me to a 4–1 victory and my first complete game. I retired the last 14 batters in a row and only eight Pirates hit the ball out of the infield. Dark said, "Nice going, Gaylord. The first victory is the roughest one." He didn't know it was my second.

May 5: I gave up my first big-league home run to Billy Williams, which was no great disgrace. He was "rookie of the year" the year before.

May 11: I suffered my first big-league defeat, 7–0, to Houston. I didn't last three innings.

June 10: I pitched two mop-up innings against St. Louis. We lost our sixth straight and fell out of first place. Alvin summoned me to his office. "Gaylord," he said, "we're in a pennant race. I think you can help yourself— and the Giants—more, going back to Tacoma and getting plenty of work. We can't use you enough right now to keep you in shape to pitch."

Traveling secretary Frankie Bergonzi gave me my airplane ticket to Tacoma the next morning. And, of course, everybody slapped me on the back and said, "We'll be seeing you soon. We'll be watching you." The Giants called up lefty Dick LeMay. At least, I had lasted long enough to make the team photo.

Going back down to the minors is the toughest thing to handle in baseball. I knew I could pitch in the big leagues. But I hadn't proved it to the manager. It didn't make me feel much better to see my old Northern League rival, Bo Belinsky, pitching a no-hitter, 2–0, for California, and my North Carolina rival, Tony Cloninger, making it with Milwaukee. I was heading in the wrong direction. Blanche, four months pregnant, packed up for Tacoma.

I was more determined than ever. I led the Pacific Coast League with a 2.48 earned run average. I had a 10–7 record, and more important, I struck out 136 batters in 156 innings. The year before with Tacoma I had struck out only 95 batters in 219 innings.

The day the season closed in Tacoma in September, pitcher Ron Herbel and I were promoted to San Francisco. I got right into the National League pennant race. The Dodgers were 95–51 and the Giants 94–51 when both clubs departed on their final eastern trips.

We opened in Cincinnati on a hot, muggy night. The trip from the West Coast was a jolt for everyone used to playing in the cooler air of San Francisco and Los Angeles. I was fresh out of Tacoma with a club that had finished next to last and suddenly found myself in a pressure cooker. I could see the difference in the guys. Fatigue lined their faces, laughter was forced from stale jokes. A thoughtless remark could set off an angry exchange. I pitched batting practice in Cincy and I could feel the strain. The first night Mays took only a couple of swings in batting practice and then retired to the clubhouse.

I had to change shirts twice that night. The sweat was pouring off me just sitting in the dugout before going out to the bullpen. At the top of the second, I heard a body tumbling to the floor of the dugout at the water fountain. It was Mays. Doc Bowman rushed to him with smelling salts. Willie opened his eyes, but seemed to see nothing.

"Take it easy, Buck, take it easy," Bowman told him.

"What happened? What's wrong with me?" Mays demanded. He sat up.

"Nothing's wrong with you. You just passed out. That's all."

Dark's face turned pale. He called to Matty Alou to loosen up. There was nothing he could say.

Larry Jansen came to Mays. "What do you say, Buck? Feeling better?"

"I don't know. I just don't feel like I want to have to move. I can. I just don't feel like it."

Doc Bowman turned quickly to us. "Get that stretcher!"

We carried Mays to the trainer's table in the club-house. An ambulance whisked him—and a pennant, we all believed—to a hospital in Cincinnati. Tests were taken, but the doctors could find nothing wrong with Willie except mental, physical and emotional exhaustion. Mays was the greatest player I ever saw. He gave 100 percent of his great talent. Mays missed his first full game of the season the next day when I got my first call in relief. I pitched one inning of a 7–2 loss.

It was that game, I think, that the veteran pitcher I was replacing cut the ball deeply with his fingernail and handed it to me and said, "Kid, I've put a hole in it for you if you want to use it. You can get another ball if you want."

"Give it to me," I said and struck out the batter. Then the cut ball was tossed out of the game. That was lesson one in pitching tricks.

I've had a lot of lessons since then, some of them strictly legal, some of them extra-legal. It's hard to draw the line. When Candy Cummings threw baseball's first curve back in the 1800's, a lot of people thought that was downright criminal.

One of the best tricks I ever heard about was the

refrigerated ball. Some baseball Columbus discovered that a frozen ball wouldn't go as far as a warm one, so before long teams that stressed pitching over hitting began slipping into the practice of refrigerating baseballs. The Chicago White Sox (rhymes with ice box) were accused of this practice during the 1965 season, especially after a doubleheader in which both teams combined got twenty-two hits, all singles. The umpire that day, Ed Hurley, admitted that the balls felt cold, but said, "They may have been stored near an air-conditioner." Sure.

Gabe Paul, who was my general manager in Cleveland before he shifted to the Yankees, says that when he was a youngster, serving as a batboy in Rochester, he had the job of putting the balls in the refrigerator. "Whenever we got ahead," Paul says, "our manager, George Stallings, would order the frozen balls into the game."

Mays' collapse made headlines across the country. It surprises me that more players don't collapse of nervous exhaustion.

Few stories reach print about the mental and emotional pressure of major-league baseball. Whenever you read that so-and-so is being taken out of the lineup for a rest, more often than not it is for a mental rest rather than a physical one. There are tragic stories of players who have suffered mental exhaustion, like Boston's Jimmy Piersall and Cleveland's Tony Horton, who had to retire at twenty-six. There are many who show the rigors of pressure in less dramatic ways, such as breaking out with hives or suffering falling hair—as Vic Davalillo did with the Indians before he was traded away. A pennant race, especially, squeezes out every bit of a man. It was obvious that whichever club won in 1962, the Dodgers or Giants, they would not have much left to battle the American League champion Yankees.

With Mays back in action, we reached the last day

of the season one game behind the Dodgers. With the score 1–1 in the eighth inning, Mays hit one of the longest homers in his career off Houston's Dick Farrell for a 2–1 victory. In the clubhouse later, we listened to the Cardinal's 1–0 victory over the Dodgers on Gene Oliver's home run, and that caused the three-game playoff which got us to the Series.

Since I wasn't eligible to play in the Series, Jansen chose me as a batting practice pitcher. I had never seen a World Series, so it was another first. Whitey Ford won the opener, 6–2. Sanford then threw a three-hit shutout at the Yankees to even things. The Series shifted to New York. Blanche was due to deliver in a couple of weeks, and when I arrived at the Roosevelt Hotel, I phoned her daddy to see how she was doing. He told me everything was fine, she was just out for a drive. That wasn't entirely a falsehood. She was out driving—trying to get to the hospital in time. A.J. didn't want to worry me with that little detail. He was afraid it might disturb my batting practice pitching. At 11:30 P.M. on the sixth of October, Amy arrived.

While not an artistic triumph for me, the season was a financial success. The Giants, after a slight hassle, agreed to pay me for a full rookie season—$7000. I got a half-share of the Series money which came to $3600, enough money to put a down payment on the George Hodges farm, worth $28,000. I was no longer the son of a tenant farmer.

I had become a landowner, at last. Not to mention a batting practice pitcher in the World Series.

. . . .

10

. . . .

Now, I ask you, would you throw a baseball as fast as you could at your own brother's head? Or would you ask someone to do that to his brother? Well, that was the question in manager Alvin Dark's mind when my brother Jim and I were opponents in an exhibition game toward the end of spring training, 1963. The Indians and the Giants have the longest spring training rivalry in baseball, dating from 1934. And headhunting, begun by players now long forgotten, somehow endured as an unbreakable habit.

Alvin managed and taught baseball as if the game had a trick up its sleeve. Either you pulled the trick, or you got the trick pulled on you. We drilled on such plays as surprise shifts and fake intentional walks. The duster was a weapon, the trick to it being when to use it. Dark's retaliatory duster usually didn't come when it was expected, like the next time at bat. That was too obvious. Dark wanted to make certain the culprit knew he was going to "get it," but never when. In a secret compartment in his wallet, Alvin kept a slip of white paper with the names of those who had unfairly hit or steam-rolled one of his players. It might take a year or even two, but that man would get his. Alvin has been out of baseball for a few years now, but I'll bet that slip of paper is still in his wallet.

Anyway, back in '63, my brother Jim and I were being ballyhooed in the San Diego papers as the match-up for the last Sunday in March. It was my regular turn, but Jim had just pitched two days before. Pitching coach Mel Harder, getting pressured by the Indians' brass and the ticket man at San Diego, asked Jim if he could go a few innings. Jim not only agreed, but he went a full nine and beat me, 4–3.

The fireworks began in the fourth inning. McCovey slammed a long homer, and on the very next pitch to Mays, Jim threw one in close and Mays took a nose dive into the dirt. Jim said later, "I always throw Mays high and tight. He doesn't like the ball there. He always goes down at anything close. Everybody knows that." Well, Alvin didn't know that. He began pacing up and down like a steam boiler itching to blow. He kept looking at me, but he said nothing. His usual response to that situation was, "You know what to do." Or, "Take care of that." That meant knock 'em down. As I went to the mound, he mumbled something.

Catcher John Romano stepped into the batter's box and I drilled him in the seat of his pants. He glared a moment and then trotted to first base and all the umpires came running to the center of the diamond and warned both managers to cease immediately. And that ended it for the time being.

Alvin smiled at me. Later in a team meeting, he said, "I could never ask a brother to hit a brother. But I knew

121

you'd take care of it, Gaylord. I appreciate what you did out there."

He didn't need to say it. A pitcher who doesn't keep the opposition "honest" is only going to suffer himself.

As the Giants and Indians barnstormed up the coast of California that spring, tempers flared several times. Indian manager Birdie Tebbetts kept Mays on the seat of his pants as we kept beating his club. Finally, Mays said to Tebbetts as he passed the Indians' bench, "Hey, Birdie, I'm too old to be knocked down." Birdie laughed and replied, "You're not old enough yet with a bat." And you know what happened the next time Mays came to the plate.

I want to make it clear that there was no viciousness in all this. It's just a part of the game. A very real part of the game. There was one unfortunate incident, however. Floyd Weaver, a young Indian pitcher that spring, had his forearm shattered by an inside pitch after an exchange of brushback throws. It ruined his career. And nobody likes to see that. One of our rookies, Jim Ray Hart, was struck by a pitch thrown by St. Louis Cardinal pitcher Bob Gibson two days after he was called up from Tacoma in July. It broke his collar bone. He appeared in only seven games with the Giants that season.

There are countless incidents involving the knock-down pitch. One that still tickles me happened in Milwaukee with Hank Fischer on the mound for the Braves. He was knocking down everybody. I came in in relief and this time it was manager Herman Franks with that vague but unmistakable order, "Let's straighten things out out there." That message arrived over the phone in the bullpen. Eventually Fischer came to the plate. He knew what was coming. On the first pitch, he turned his back to me and crouched down with his arms over his head. The pitch hit him right in the seat of his pants. He dropped his bat and hollered, "Ooohh, that smarts." And the crowd roared.

I got involved in a knock-'em-down-drag-'em-out with Sandy Koufax once. Now in this confrontation, I was way overmatched. Sandy was throwing a pea-sized baseball and I was throwing a regulation ball. When I came to bat in the sixth, Sandy, who never liked to throw at a batter, fired a fast ball about a foot over my head. I collapsed to the ground like a cut redwood tree and pleaded with the ump, "Aren't you going to put a stop to this before somebody gets killed? Me?" Against Koufax, it was already out of hand as far as I was concerned.

The rules have been tightened up since the early '60s, but the "brushback pitch," the "rib roaster," the "knee knocker" and the bean ball exist in the game today just as surely as there are some pitchers greasing up baseballs. All are very much a part of the grand old ball game. But a dangerous part. A pitcher deliberately aiming for a batter's head may be attempting homicide. In 1920, Carl Mays accidentally struck Cleveland batter Ray Chapman who died a few days later without regaining consciousness. Recent history is full of cases of damaged careers because of beanings. It took Baltimore center fielder Paul Blair two years and hypnosis to regain his confidence after having his jaw broken by a pitch in 1971. Don Mincher was hit in the face by a Sam McDowell fast ball, lost several teeth and suffered a fractured jaw. He had dizzy spells the next two years. Tony Conigliaro had his vision ruined and career ended by a bean ball. Every pitcher respects the courage it takes for a batter to stand up against a blazing fast ball and crackling curve. Some batters in the big leagues now can't stomach being thrown at. And the pitchers know who they are.

The season of 1963 was the worst in my entire career, statistically, artistically and emotionally. I had a 1–6 record and 4.03 earned run average. Maybe it was the play-off goof, but Dark had no confidence in me at all. I was banished to the bullpen except for three starting assignments in a total of 76 innings pitched. The season included a brief trip back to Tacoma where I pitched one game before another recall to the Giants. My career was ceasing to be a career.

I had a good spring, but Marichal, Sanford, O'Dell and Pierce were the starters, with Larsen and Bolin doing the spot starting. I was very unhappy. I griped a lot to Jansen. He kept pleading with me to bide my time and be ready when I got the chance. I fought being tagged a relief pitcher. A sportswriter asked me my status when the season opened:

"Will you be spot starting?"

"Nope."

"Short man?"

"Nope."

"Long man?"

"Nope. Garbage man."

I was mop-up man, perhaps befitting the $1000 raise I got to $8000 that year. I started off well in relief, allowing only two earned runs in 26 innings (0.69 ERA) covering nine appearances. I finally won my first game late in May. It was a 4–3 victory in 11 innings over the Mets when everybody was beating them. I pitched the final two innings. Joe Amalfitano won my only victory of the year with a home run. I was on the mound so seldom, it was getting embarrassing.

Adding to my embarrassment were the articles on how pitching was dominating baseball that season. In less than seven weeks of play there had been two no-hitters, four near no-hitters lost in the eighth or ninth innings, 77 shutouts and no less than 68 ball games in which one team got three hits or less. Players and managers all over baseball were crediting the spitball for the pitcher's domination. A quick glance at my rising earned run average absolved me from any suspicion of juicing up a baseball. The truth is, I didn't know anything about the spitter then.

Others, it was said, did know. It was suggested that Whitey Ford, probably the best lefty in the American League, had refined the pitch to the point that his name in the box score ought to carry an asterisk: *Does well on wet track. Ford was accused of wetting up a ball and giving it a mud pack as well. Some claimed that Whitey was also cutting the ball with a ring on his finger.

Other American League pitchers whose names kept bobbing up in dugout conversations on the spitball were Pete Ramos of Cleveland, Earl Wilson of the Boston Red Sox, Jim Bunning of the Detroit Tigers, Ron Kline of the Washington Senators and Jim Brosnan of the Chicago White Sox. In our league, it was the champ of them all, Drysdale, and Ron Perranoski of the Dodgers, Bob Friend of the Pirates and Dick Farrell of Houston.

There were other substances in wide use, such as pine tar. After pitching a ball game in Chavez Ravine, Angels pitcher Bo Belinsky left a group of reporters for a moment to hand a small tube to his pitching teammate, Bob Turley.

"Say, thanks for that stuff, Bob. It worked real fine."

"What stuff?" the reporters asked.

"Bob gave me some sticky stuff for my hand," said Bo, gratefully.

"That's supposed to be illegal," a writer said.

"Give me that stuff and keep your mouth shut," snapped Turley, looking to the ceiling. "How dumb can you get?"

Mostly, though, the illegal substance was just plain spit. Gene Mauch, manager of the Phillies, said, "There are 100 pitchers in the National League. And I'd say that 25 of them throw the spitter to some degree. Why, I've even got a couple who throw it myself." When the manager of the Kansas City Athletics, Ed Lopat, was asked if his pitchers were throwing the spitter, he answered, "Not any more than anyone else." Chicago White Sox manager Al Lopez pointed the accusing finger at Dean Chance of the Los Angeles Angels, saying he saw him throw a spitter that would have pleased Burleigh Grimes (maybe the greatest legal spitballer of all time.)

With both of us throwing only legal pitches, it was

a bad summer for the Perrys. The Indians traded Jim to the Minnesota Twins for Jack Kralick—and $100,000 which didn't get into the papers. Jim finished 9–9 that season. He won only 45 games the next five seasons until he developed a screwball and sinker (not like mine) and became a 20-game winner.

The Giants fell out of the top spot in June and wound up the season in third place. Al Dark was struggling over a decision about McCovey and Cepeda. Both belonged on first base, but one had to play left field. But which one? That was Dark's problem. I had plenty of my own. I thought I belonged on the mound, but I wasn't out there much. And when I was out there, sometimes my performances weren't quite good enough to convince Dark.

I guess Dark had other things on his mind—like Maury Wills, for instance. When Wills was with the Dodgers, and I was with the Giants, we were always worrying about him. He was the greatest base-stealer in the history of the game; in 1962, my first season up, Maury stole 104 bases, a record that could last forever. That same year, Dark earned himself a nickname: The Swamp Fox. When the Dodgers came to Candlestick Park for a key series, the ball park was a swamp—especially around home plate, first base and second base. The umpires seemed a bit surprised; Alvin said he was, too. "The wind blew a lot of dirt off the field yesterday," he said. "I guess the ground crew just watered a little too much."

Matty Schwab, the head of the ground crew, backed up Alvin's story. "We were watering the infield late in the afternoon," he said, "and we didn't notice a leak in the hose."

Schwab also explained that because of the excess watering, he had sprinkled a lot of sand around the bases. He figured that might absorb the water.

It certainly touched off a lot of jokes. Ron Fairly, the Dodger first baseman, said he deserved a two-stroke handicap for playing in a water hazard. The next day, Fairly came to the park in hip boots.

The band at Candlestick joined in the fun. They played "Love Letters in the Sand."

It wasn't Wills' favorite tune. He didn't steal another base at Candlestick that year. I wish Dark had spent as much time thinking about me as he did thinking about Maury.

The morning of August 4, 1963, I was reading a Chicago newspaper in the lobby of the Edgewater Beach Hotel. There was a headline about the U.S. and Russia signing a nuclear test ban treaty. I felt a tap on my shoulder and turned. There was Frankie Bergonzi, the traveling secretary, holding another airplane ticket to Tacoma.

"Not again," I moaned, as if I were surprised. Frankie sent the guys down and Dark called them up.

"Sorry," Frankie said sadly, "we're calling up Frank Linzy. You'll be back. Next time to stay." Linzy was 16–6 with a 1.55 ERA at Springfield in the Eastern League.

I phoned Blanche and she began packing again. We left the next day from San Francisco on that lonely 1200-mile drive to Tacoma, Washington. Without Blanche, I might have kept driving to Fairbanks, Alaska. I pitched one game at Tacoma, beat Hawaii with a three-hitter and got called back up to San Francisco—special delivery, by airplane.

Blanche had to pack up again and drive herself and Amy 1200 miles. It was the fourth time she packed up and moved our belongings in the eight months since spring training began. The reason for my hasty recall was pitcher Jim Duffalo. He had split a finger. When I arrived, the Giants were still in the race, but the Dodgers seemed to be pulling away. Dark, who did such a brilliant job in 1962, was running into discontent. The grumbling had begun.

It was the first game of a doubleheader with the Cubs

on Labor Day before 34,590 fans. The Cubs jumped off to a 2–0 lead in the first inning on Ron Santo's single. They got another in the third, and with two on and two out, Dark called me in for starter Bob Bolin. Mays hauled down a long fly to end the inning. In the fourth, we rallied for three runs and had the bases loaded when Willie came to the plate. The fans were on their feet rooting for him to do it again.

Mays did it again. But not what anybody expected. He stepped into the batter's box, took a couple of loosening-up swings and then stood upright as if struck by an unseen bullet. He bent over and crumpled to the ground. It was another emotional and physical collapse. The crowd suddenly went silent. The whole squad was out there and Mays was helped back onto his feet and walked to the dugout. The crowd responded with nervous applause, and Mays was sent home to bed for three days. It was a tough season for him, again playing almost every day and carrying the club. He had a .245 batting average in June, but still wound up the season batting .314.

I gave up three more runs the next inning and the Cubs beat us 7–5 for my sixth and final loss of the season. We lost the second game as well, Santo hitting a pair of homers, and the pennant race was over. Later, when Mays was recovered and his old effervescent self, I told him, "Every time you see me coming back from Tacoma, you faint. It ought to be in your contract that the next time they ship me out, you receive two days' warning before I return to the club." He laughed and went out and hit a home run against the Dodgers that afternoon. It was my biggest contribution to the Giants that year: relaxing Mays enough to hit a home run.

When the season ended, I felt that my baseball future was in serious danger. I was a six-year professional, and the best I could do over a full season was one victory with the Giants and one victory with Tacoma. Marichal talked his club in the Dominican Republic into signing me for winter ball. Blanche was pregnant that winter. Her doctor would not allow her to travel. We would have to be separated, but there was no choice. I had to find myself, or, at least, see if there was anything to find. The $1500-a-month salary plus expenses helped the budget. But pitching, after the few innings I had worked with the Giants, was vital.

I picked up where I left off with the Giants and lost my first five games in the Dominican Republic for a record of 2–11 overall in 1963. I was about to be cut by the club when I won my next five in a row and went on to lead the league in strike-outs. That did wonders for my confidence. It was a rather quiet winter off the field. Not one riot. After my experiences in Mexico in the Texas League, I chose an apartment located under a drugstore, one block east of the police station and one block west of the main hospital in Santo Domingo. During the playoffs in Venezuela, gamblers kidnapped Caracas' best soccer player. Fearing the same thing, we were motored to the ball park in armored cars and were assigned guards with submachine guns. It was the first time I took a shower with a bodyguard.

While we were down there, I read about the big trade between the Giants and Milwaukee: the Braves sent us catcher Del Crandall and pitchers Bob Shaw and Bob Hendley for outfielder Felipe Alou, catcher Ed Bailey, pitcher Billy Hoeft and infielder Ernie Bowman. Once again the Giants were trading for pitching. I was sorry to see Shaw and Hendley coming to San Francisco. I should have rejoiced.

11

It wasn't just coincidence that almost every season the Giants traded for pitching: in 1959, they picked up Jack Sanford and Sam Jones; in 1960, Billy Loes and Billy O'Dell; in 1962, Billy Pierce and Don Larsen. Now in 1964, it was Bob Shaw and Bob Hendley. I didn't know at first how profitable that last deal would be for me.

I was hopeful of breaking into the starting rotation in 1964. After all, I was the strike-out king of the Dominican Republic, and I'd finished the season there with five straight victories. Coach Larry Jansen and I set to work on the sharp slider. My arsenal till then had been the fast ball, the changeup, the curve ball and the gopher ball.

One day early in training camp, I happened by Shaw as he was heating up. I noticed something odd about some of his throws. They arrived at the plate in a very unnatural way, shooting in about thigh-high, then dipping to the ankles.

I hesitated to approach a bona fide big-leaguer with some questions. But I remembered what Daddy used to say, "If you don't open your mouth, you can't eat."

"Bob, would you show me how you do that?" I finally asked.

"Do what?" he said.

"Make a ball go down like that."

"It's just a natural sinker."

"Would you show me how you hold it?"

Shaw must have taken a liking to me. At least, he figured I wasn't a cop. He wet his two fingers, placed them on top of the ball, wound and fired. And down it went. "This is all there is to it, Gaylord," he said. "But it takes a lot of work. You got to know how much to apply, where, how to hold the ball and control it, and, most important, how to load it up without anybody seeing you. It's a dangerous pitch. You can hurt your arm. If you get caught, you can get into trouble. And it'll take a long time to master it. But, if you can learn it, it'll make you a lot of money."

"I sure do want to try," I said.

Most pitchers experiment with a spitter but soon give it up. If you don't throw it correctly, it is just like a hanging curve ball—a gopher pitch. It took me the rest of that season and the next to master it in every way. Shaw and I were inseparable, spitball buddies, so to speak.

But we had to be discrete. I didn't want Dark to know we were working on it until it was perfected. Shaw didn't want Jansen to think he was moving in on the pitching coach's job. But I definitely needed another pitch immediately. The slider was coming very slowly. If I could master the spitter in the meantime, I could get myself into the starting rotation and let the slider develop as I went along, I reasoned.

131

It was ironic that nine years later Shaw would be coming to me for advice on the greaser. Shaw only knew about the spitter. During the 1972 World Series in Oakland, he asked me to meet him for lunch. He had been named pitching coach of the Milwaukee Brewers. He greeted me warmly and said, "Gaylord, would you tell me how you throw it?"

"Throw what?" I asked.

"C'mon, Gaylord, the greaser."

"Why Bob, you know I wouldn't cheat. That's my fork ball."

"I've got some kids over in Milwaukee who might be able to learn the super-slider, or whatever you call it."

"Bob, I owe you a favor all right. I'll tell you, but if I do, you got to promise me you'll never use it against Cleveland. And when I'm pitching against you, I don't want you running to the umpires, telling them what places to look for. And if you ever repeat this conversation I'll deny I ever said anything."

"Gaylord, don't worry, it's between me and you. I'm not telling anybody. Now, where do you get it from?"

I told him. I owed him that much.

While I was working on my infant spitter in the spring of 1964, I remember Mays teasing me about it in batting practice. "Gaylord, what you puttin' on that ball? C'mon, what you doin'?"

"What you talking about, Willie? I ain't doing nothing."

"I'll do my batting against somebody else. I'm not going to get my uniform splashed with your juice," Mays laughed.

I had stage fright the first few times I experimented with the spitter in ball games. I was afraid of being caught and afraid of what might happen if I didn't load the ball correctly.

Once I tried it out in a spring training game against

Cleveland, against ex-Giant Leon Wagner. Wags was some kind of hitter until his eyes went bad on him. He was the only batter I ever saw who left the ground to swing at a pitched baseball. I mean both feet in the air at once. I threw him one of my apprentice dew drops, and just as he was leaving the ground to go get the ball, it started dipping. His swing was already underway, but he tried to change course in midstream. He switched so violently his helmet flew off; he missed the ball, but fouled off his helmet.

Wags started laughing, and pretty soon Haller was laughing and so was umpire John Rice and both benches. Wags looked at me. "Hey, Gaylord," he said, "what is a nice boy like you doing a thing like that for?"

"Wags, what are you talking about?" I said.

"You just put my swing back five years."

Catcher Tommy Haller and Jansen knew what I was doing as we approached the opening of the season. Neither said a word to Dark. I didn't want Dark to think I was clowning around with something illegal, instead of working on the slider. Jansen was concerned about the risk of injuring my arm while learning the spitter and the slider. But I explained to him, "Larry, I've got to take the risk now, or there might be no risk to take."

I had a good spring, but Dark was unimpressed. Finally, coach Herman Franks interceded for me. "Alvin, I like the way Perry throws," Herman said. "He's big, strong and has a lot more stuff to go with a much better fast ball. I like the way he works." Herman knew about my dew drop.

"He looks the same to me," Alvin replied.

"I'd like to see us give him another real look as a starter."

"Herman, he really hasn't shown me he can."

And that ended the conversation.

The Giants offered me the same contract in 1964 that I had the year before—$8000. They agreed to up it to

$9000 when I told them we were expecting another child and that I would go to winter ball to improve my pitching.

I wasn't used through the month of April. In fact, I was never even asked to warm up during a game. Shaw and Franks and the quiet chats with Jansen kept me from taking that one step off the Golden Gate Bridge. The only good news I had during this time was the birth of my daughter, Beth, on May 4. Two days later I made my first relief appearance against the Cubs. I shut them out and struck out three of the last five I faced, including Lou Brock and Ron Santo.

But it made no difference to Dark. I didn't get a starting call until May 23 against the Pittsburgh Pirates. I blew it, giving up a two-run home run to Gerry Lynch and another two-run shot to Roberto Clemente. I got another mid-game shower and my first loss after two victories in relief.

I pitched a week later for two shutout innings. The slider was slowly coming; the spitter was working on the sidelines, but I was afraid to put it on public display in a real game.

I don't know when I would've gotten up the nerve to use the spitter if we hadn't hit that long day in Shea Stadium. And then it was only because my back was to the wall and Dark had been ejected from the game. If they hit me, Dark would never know what it was they hit. After a couple innings, Herman Franks, who had taken over, knew what I was up to. He told me, "Gaylord, I don't care what you're doing out there as long as you keep getting them out. You go out there and win."

Those ten innings I worked in the 23-inning game became the turning point in my career. There was frustration still ahead, but my career finally began to move.

Dark became more friendly. He smiled at me and said, "Hello Gaylord. What you got, a new pitch? You look as happy as a kid with a new toy." He fully approved.

134

Still, Dark considered me more valuable in the bullpen and I didn't get my next starting call until a month later, at Candlestick against those same Mets.

I rang up my first major-league shutout by gunning down the Mets, 5–0. Writers started asking me what miracle had overtaken me after my 1–6 record and 4.03 earned run average of the previous year. I told them, "I'm getting more pitching in. Shaw's been working with me on little things. Like pitching to corners instead of just throwing. Like getting my arm up and getting more power instead of dropping my elbow."

I'll be forever grateful to Haller who put up with me that first season or two I began wetting the ball. I started out really slobbering on the old apple. Sometimes, I'm ashamed to admit, you could see the spray flying off the ball in flight. One time Haller came out to the mound and pleaded, "Gay, please cut down on the load. I'm getting drenched."

In late July, Jack Sanford underwent a ten-hour operation to repair an artery blockage that took feeling from his arm. Marichal developed back problems. It was the chance I needed, and on August 4, 1964, I became a regular starter, a job I've held to this day. Ironically, it was the Mets again, in a game we lost 4–3. I went ten innings and allowed only one earned run.

Maybe giving me a starting role was part of Dark's desperation. He was already in hot water over some disparaging remarks about black and Latin players, and the club had faded. He would have been fired earlier except that the front office didn't want to let him go in the midst of the controversy.

I won five and lost three as a starter the rest of the season and finished with a 12–11 record and a 2.75 earned run average. The Cubs knocked the stuffings out of me in the last game of the '64 season. I lasted only two innings and gave up six runs. But Al Dark lasted only two innings

135

more than me. The phone rang in the dugout in the fifth. It was Mr. Stoneham telling Dark he was fired as manager of the Giants.

I couldn't feel too sorry for Alvin, but I could understand a little how he felt. It was only a few months earlier that he must have thought, at times, of letting me go. I'll be forever grateful to Bob Shaw for wising—and wetting —me up.

12

In late July of 1965, my career was in another recession. Working for a new manager, Herman Franks, I had a 7–8 record which was getting worse. And my spitball wasn't getting any attention. Bob Shaw's was getting all the publicity.

After Shaw beat the Braves, 7–2, Milwaukee manager Bobby Bragan admitted to the newspapers that he had ordered his pitchers to throw spitters to the Giants. Bragan proudly boasted that the five Milwaukee pitchers threw "between 75 and 80 spitters." Bragan had been Shaw's manager two years before at Milwaukee, and Bragan said he wanted to prove that "the umpires won't stop anyone from throwing the spitter." He said, "I told the pitchers to throw the spitter and to make no pretense of hiding it. The umpires didn't say anything about it."

Shaw was beautiful. He replied, cap in hand, "I don't even know how to throw a spitball. I wouldn't even know how to do it. I've heard guys talk about it, but I never could learn." Umpire Frank Secory, boss of the four-man umpire team that night, said, "If any pitcher threw a spitter, I didn't see it." Bob Sadowski, who replaced starter Hank Fischer for Milwaukee, said he threw five spitters. "They let me get away with it, so I might as well take advantage of it. I'm going to work on it now," said Sadowski. He needed some work; he gave up six runs on six hits in three innings. The next day, Bragan ordered up more spitters (85 by his own count) against us. This time Marichal defeated the Braves, 3–1, and Bragan charged that Marichal threw spitters, too. That was ridiculous. Some people thought Bragan might be disciplined by league president Warren Giles for ordering an illegal pitch, but Giles provided the perfect response: "My only comment is if the Braves' pitchers threw all those spitballs, they apparently weren't very effective." Case closed. Complaint dismissed.

(Several years later, when Billy Martin tried a tactic similar to Bragan's, the American League president, Joe Cronin, didn't react as wittily, or as well. Martin's ploy ended up costing him his job.)

Mauch, the Philadelphia manager, used to stay in the third-base coaching box to get a closer look at Shaw. "I don't *think* Shaw throws a spitter, I know he does," said Mauch. "But as long as the umpires won't stop him, I don't blame him a bit." All the time my spitball was being completely ignored. It couldn't have been a very good one then.

The spitball issue raged that entire season. President Giles seemed the least disturbed about it. As if quoting from scripture, he said, "It's a phase through which we often have passed. I'm not naive enough to think the spitter is not being used, or that it hasn't been since it was ruled illegal many, many years ago. But to prove it is something else. My umpires have their instructions—enforce the rule. But it isn't that simple." When asked about Bragan's brash statements that he ordered his pitchers to throw the illegal spitter, Giles said, "I've learned over the years not to take Bobby too seriously."

Later that season, I found myself accused of using stickum. Milwaukee's third-base coach Jo-Jo White asked umpire John Kibler to take a good look at a ball I'd thrown, and Kibler threw the ball out of the game. The other umpires then conferred with Kibler, discussing the situation. Frankly, it felt kind of nice to receive some attention for a change. But for stickum?

After the game, Brash Bobby was at it again. "It looks like anything goes now," Bragan said. "The umpires won't do anything. The spitball has become recognized as an accepted thing. Now the sticky ball. Perry had the sticky substance in his glove. The umpires examined everything but that."

White said, "All I know is that the ball was sticky."

That 1965 season was a tough one for me. I wasn't even getting the right accusations. My won-lost percentage shot down, and my earned run average shot up. I had nobody to blame but myself. I came to camp with a $15,000 contract (up from $9,000), with the manager on my side, a starting job and confidence in my fast ball. I wound up 8–12 with an ERA of 4.18.

I acted like a real hot dog. I found myself arguing with umpires, fuming when I made a bad pitch and bristling at any error behind me. And I'd annoy my teammates by taking forever to deliver the pitch. I just never realized how bad I looked and how much it hurt me. Once, after fuming in the locker room, I did a real bush thing: I telephoned upstairs to complain about an "error" that an official scorer had called a hit off me. That was the season I picked up clubhouse man Eddie Logan and put him head-first into a rubbish can. I was blaming everybody else but me for my failure.

It seems, though, that whenever times were rough, there was always someone around to give me a lift. Willie Mays came by one afternoon to talk. "Gaylord," he told me, "your temper and your slowness to get ready to pitch are hurting you with your teammates and the umpires. Remember, the less time we're in the field, the longer we're at bat. The longer we stand around, the more of an edge we lose. If you could just speed up your game, it would make us more alert. Here we are waiting for the pitch and you are fiddlin' around. You're going to your hat four or five times, stepping off and on the rubber. I know you're trying to decoy the opposing team and set 'em up. But don't forget your own players behind you. We see you're not ready, then we relax. Then you pitch the ball, when we're not ready. You have to cut the stalling, so we can help you more. The umpires appreciate a fast game, too. They'll do a better job if you work faster."

Just a few minutes with Mays got me straightened out. I noticed my defense perk up and that the umpires began giving *me* the corners of the plate.

Coach Wes Westrum, maybe one of the best sign stealers ever, gave me some helpful advice, too. I was tipping my spitter. He told me about not tossing that elm tablet around or shifting it when I was going to wet up. "They'll be watching your cheeks for any motion and know what's coming," he warned.

Maybe it was all the clubhouse turmoil the year before with Dark, but in 1965, the Giants were a solid happy unit from the first day of spring training. Herman Franks and I hit it off like no manager I had before or since. He was relaxed and easy to communicate with. He'd sit down and discuss how he and his players could improve together. In his four seasons as manager, we were the winningest club in baseball in either league. Our only flaw was we always finished second, a situation that eventually led Herman to resign.

Herman had a long talk with me midway in the 1965 season. I had pitched myself out of a starting job. Yet he had time to talk, to help a greatly confused young pitcher.

"Gaylord, you're perfect, aren't you?"

"What do you mean, skip?"

"I mean you don't make mistakes on that mound, throw to the wrong spot or anything?"

"Of course I do. You been watching me, Herm, ain't you?"

"Yes I have. I've been seeing a lot I don't like. And I've got to tell you about it before it's too late. It's all that anger at the umpires, your teammates, yourself, the fans. It's a lot of crap. Right now things are not going your way because of bad luck and you're making it worse. Is anybody thinking better or performing better when he's boiling mad? Stop feeling sorry for yourself and things that happen around you. Let your catcher do the arguing with the umpire. And stop grumbling about your defense. You are the biggest part of the defense. I want you to watch other pitchers when they get mad. See how it looks and see what happens to their effectiveness."

I'd heard the same lecture at Williamston High a decade earlier. Hadn't I learned anything? My struggle to keep a governor on my emotions started coming to me along with improvement on the spitter and the slider. So I let Haller holler and I began to pitch well, although not too frequently and usually in relief.

Not many Dodger and Giant baseball fans will forget August 22, 1965. It was one of those uneasy afternoons. Trouble seemed to ride the wind. And, of course, there was wind. It was Candlestick Park and, as usual, the Dodgers and the Giants were in the thick of a pennant fight, almost in a tie. The snarling began early.

Marichal flattened Maury Wills in the second inning and Ron Fairly was dusted in the third, with the Dodgers ahead, 2–1. When Marichal came to bat in the bottom of the third, everybody was ready for something to happen. Koufax was on the mound. Sandy didn't like bean ball wars because he could kill somebody with one of his fast balls. And his control was so good, it was a dead giveaway when he let a pitch "get away."

Koufax pitched Marichal down the middle of the plate. After the second pitch, a called strike, catcher John Roseboro's throw back to the mound whistled past Marichal's right ear. Marichal stiffened and glared at Roseboro who ignored him. Koufax threw again and Roseboro fired back to the mound again. This time his throw ticked Marichal's ear. It was a duster from the rear, of all things. Roseboro knew Koufax wasn't going to deck Marichal.

"What do you think you're doing?" Marichal demanded.

Roseboro said, "Get in and bat."

Suddenly, Roseboro rose up and came at Marichal, who swung his bat down on Roseboro's head, opening a two-inch gash. The fight was on. Plate umpire Shag Crawford and Koufax ran at Marichal to wrestle for the bat. Mays tackled Roseboro, pleading for peace. Then Mays saved Tito Fuentes from more trouble by tackling him and pulling another bat from his hand. Without Mays' efforts, there might have been a full-scale riot. It took 15 minutes to restore order. Marichal was ejected for swinging a weapon and Roseboro retired to the clubhouse for first aid. Crawford said, "If Marichal had only used his fists, there would have been no ejection. You have to understand the tension in a tight pennant race. But there is no place for swinging a bat."

The following day, Giles suspended Marichal for nine days and eight playing dates and fined him $1750. In addition, he barred Marichal from accompanying the club to Los Angeles for two games in early September. A few weeks later, Roseboro brought suit against Marichal and the Giants for $110,000. He complained, "I've been getting migraine headaches and my neck has been stiff." A settlement in the suit was reached five years later for $7500.

I hardly pitched the final two months of the season. My last start was in August—an ineffective one. Herman called me into his office the last day of the season. I had an 8–12 record.

"I'm not sure what to do with you," Herman said to me. "I've got some clubs asking about you. I can trade you if you want to get traded. Do you want to?"

"No, that isn't what I want," I replied. "I've learned a lot about me after having this kind of season. I like the Giants and I like San Francisco. All I want is another chance to pitch for the Giants."

"Okay," Herman smiled. "That's what I wanted to know. We just want you to come to camp next spring using the talent you have. We're pulling for you to make it, kid."

13

By opening day, 1966, I had my spitter, my slider and my temper in good shape, but the thing I needed more was patience. It took me a while to get my chance. Once I got it, it didn't take me too long to impress the National League.

One of my best days came late in June. I defeated the Atlanta Braves, 3–1, my first victory over them in eight tries, and I struck out 12, a career high. I did it with both feet wrapped in tape. My left ankle was tightly wrapped because of a severe sprain that had disabled me for 15 days. The right foot was bandaged because of a calcium deposit on the instep. If I'd been a horse back home, they'd have shot me. That victory over the Braves lifted my season record to 11–1 and lowered my earned run average to 2.14.

Writers were asking, "What gives with Perry?" Bobby Bragan, the Braves' manager, had the answer: "I'd say Perry's pitching with a lot more finesse than he was a year ago. He's got the good fast ball, the good slider and the good *spitter*."

I had arrived! For the first time, I had been publicly accused of throwing the spitter.

Me and the spitter and the slider formed an unholy trinity in 1966. After a dismal record the year before, I was suddenly challenging Sandy Koufax and Juan Marichal for the league lead in victories. The papers were calling me an overnight sensation. The Giants' front office knew and I knew it had taken me eight years to become an overnight sensation.

After my talk with Herman Franks the final day of that terrible 1965 season, I spent a few days with Daddy down on the farm. I helped finish the harvest and got the land ready for the next season. I sweated in the fields just as I had done as a boy, alone with the crops and my thoughts. It was there I discovered the right perspective on my baseball and myself.

"Gaylord, did you ever stop a hurricane by getting mad at it?" Daddy asked. "Talking or thinking angry about your tobacco crop won't make it grow better. Hard work will." I got the message. I finally realized that mistakes are going to happen. I'm going to make them. The other guys are going to make them. It was time to grow up. I was twenty-seven years old and possessed a grand total of 24 victories in four major-league seasons.

I flew home to Blanche and the kids in San Mateo, California, determined to make myself a winner. I sharpened up my decoy moves on the spitter and I even practiced swinging a bat for an hour a night. I knew Marichal helped himself with his bat: I had just been hurting me with mine.

For the first time I left the family at home and reported to spring training three weeks early. I got out to the park every morning at 8:30, two hours before I was due. Before anyone else arrived, I put in an hour and a half of running and calisthenics and worked on my spitter, practicing my decoys in front of a six-foot mirror, and throwing to any minor-league catcher I could corral.

I made some important changes that spring. I began throwing straight overhand to give my pitches more power and to make the spitter break down both in and outside the plate. I began taking five minutes of pepper before pitching and starting my warmup about five minutes earlier than I had. I'd gone through my record and discovered I always had trouble in the first three innings. I worked to make sure I was warm and loose and ready right at the start. It was Marichal's strategy to start a game very strong to gain the psychological edge, and I knew he was right.

One day out in the outfield at training camp, I threw a slider, and Larry Jansen yelled, "That's it. Do it again. You've finally got it." And that *was* it, after working on it for two seasons. I had finally mastered the slider. It wasn't in the same league as my spitter, but at last I had everything together: a fast ball, a curve, a slider that broke in two directions, and a spitter that broke down over the inside or outside corners of the plate. Publicly, I just bragged about my new hard slider.

I quickly became the best pitcher in training camp. Marichal and Shaw were holding out for more money, so I moved into the starting rotation. I won five games and lost none in Arizona, and Herman promised me I'd start the second game of the season. But when the season opened, Marichal, Bob Bolin, Ron Herbel and Bob Shaw started the first four games. Then came the same rotation again. I didn't face a batter in the first seven games.

I went to Jansen. "What did I come to spring training for so early?" I said. "Why did I do all that work to get myself ready to open the season?"

"Gaylord, I know it doesn't seem fair. But those other fellows had pretty good seasons last year. That carries some weight. Stay ready and you can be sure your chance will come."

I stayed ready. I made batting practice my own personal war. I pitched like it was a regulation ball game. The hitters didn't like it, but I just couldn't let all that hard work go to waste. I only had to wait a few days more. That wasn't bad. After all, the Giants had been waiting eight years for me.

On April 19, against the Cubs in Wrigley Field, Herman went through four pitchers before calling on me in what can only be described as desperation. I pitched two and two-thirds shutout innings, struck out four and won, 11–10.

Four days later, I got my first start, in Houston, and won a four-hitter, 2–1. I told the folks back in San Francisco how I felt on a post-game radio show: "I guess that will show Herman and the Giants I can be a starting pitcher." My remark was picked up by a San Francisco reporter who made it seem that Herman and I were feuding. That wasn't true, but I sure did want a chance to show off my slicky new toy. Herman told the press, "Hell, I'd like to have three more guys say things like that and mean it like he did."

I won my first five, and then the Pirates invaded Candlestick for a three-game series. I had a slightly sore right foot that had been bothering me on and off for two seasons. We were down by a run in the third when I singled and went to second on a bunt. Favoring my right foot, I slid late and jammed my left ankle. It ached, but I wasn't coming out. I singled again in the seventh with the score tied at two-all. Herman saw me hobbling. I didn't know which sore foot to put down. Herman called time. I waved him back. But he kept coming. He had only one question: "Can you run hard?"

"I don't think so," I admitted.

"Then get out of here," said Herman. "I want a run right here."

It turned out to be brilliant strategy. Don Mason pinch-ran, and Tom Haller singled him home and we went on to win, 5–2. The Candlestick crowd booed Herman for taking me out, but they didn't know about my ankle. The next day, I was put on the 15-day disabled list; I had a sprained ankle and I was on crutches for a week. I missed six starts, and that just may have cost us the pennant— that plus the trade of Orlando Cepeda to the Cardinals (for Ray Sadecki) and the sale of Bob Shaw to, of all teams, the Mets.

Ironically, it was the day I came off the disabled list that my tutor—Shaw—was sold to make room for me on the roster. (Shaw, at the time, was only 1–4 with a 6.67 earned run average; he wound up winning eleven games with the Mets.) I shut out the Cubs in my first game back and evened my career record at 31–31. From that point on, through the 1973 season, I never missed a start, more than 300 calls in a row. Late in June, I beat Cincinnati, 10–0, a two-hit, no-walk game that gave me a string of only three runs allowed in 31 innings. I was pleased, and so were the Giants. They very quietly gave me a $5000 raise, up to $20,000 for the season.

As further tangible proof of my progress, I was named to the National League All-Star team. I was one of the six Giants on the squad, and I must've been the most excited.

It was 105 degrees at Busch Stadium for the 1966 All-Star game, but Sandy Koufax, the starting pitcher, was preparing himself as if he were in Candlestick Park, or the Arctic.

"How can you stand the smell of that, much less the heat?" I asked Sandy. He was getting capsolin rubbed on his arm.

"Gaylord, you get used to it," said Koufax. "I *have to* use it to pitch."

"It makes my eyes water and my nose burn just standing here," I said.

"Sometimes," said Sandy, "the pain on my skin keeps my mind off the pain in my elbow."

Because of his arthritic problem, he had to keep his arm blazing hot. The perspiration rolled off him on the mound, which gave me an idea. I already knew that my super-sinker was easier to load on humid days. With Sandy's capsolin formula, I could be hot and humid even on freezing days. I became a convert to capsolin. The Giants' trainer, Leo Hughes, suggested I use a thin undercoating of baby oil until I became used to the hot liniment. I started out with half a tube and, over the years, worked my way up to three tubes of capsolin a game. I guess I've become a tough old goat.

That was a terrific All-Star game for me. I not only learned the secret of capsolin, I got myself an All-Star victory. I pitched the ninth and tenth innings, shut out the American League on one hit and got credit for the win. A funny thing happened to Richie Allen: he almost missed the game. When he showed up—just in time—he told us what had happened. He'd gone to the wrong ball park—old Sportsman's Field—instead of new Busch Stadium. Willie McCovey wouldn't buy that explanation. "Don't give me that," said Willie. "We know you went out with Jim Ray Hart last night. Jim Ray got to you *again*."

McCovey said "again" deliberately. Four years earlier, Allen and Hart went into the last game of the season in the Eastern League neck-and-neck for the batting title. Hart was ahead by two points. Allen got an idea.

"Let's go out for a couple of drinks tonight," Allen suggested to Jim Ray the night before their teams met in the final game.

"Okay," said Jim Ray.

They went to a bar Richie knew and he put down ten dollars, all the money he had. He figured that if he could get Jim Ray a little high, Jim Ray wouldn't hit anything the next day. Allen whispered to the bartender, "Keep bringing drinks till that ten dollars is gone."

When the ten was gone, Richie was ready to leave. He felt real good.

"Okay, Jim Ray, let's go," said Richie, with a smile.

Hart shook his head. "Uh-uh, let's have some more," he said. Hart grabbed Richie's arm and put his own ten dollars on the bar. "We drink this and then we go." Suddenly, Richie realized he might be in a little trouble. He was. The next day Richie went oh-for-four and Jim Ray went four-for-four. Jim Ray laughed for nine innings. He won the batting title by eight percentage points.

Both Jim Ray and Richie came in as pinch hitters in the All-Star game. Both were cold sober. Both struck out.

For a long time that year, despite my ankle injury, it looked like I might win 25. Late in July, I struck out 15 Phillies, just one short of the all-time Giant record, set 60 years earlier by a pretty fair pitcher named Christy Matthewson. I had my old dew drop working good that night. I struck out nine batters in the first four innings and had a no-hitter till the eighth. In the ninth, I struck out Richie Allen, Bill White and Tony Gonzalez—each one on a called third-strike spitter. The papers said I had everybody swinging at my hard slider. But Allen, who struck out four times, was a little smarter. He said, "Perry did it with the best spitter I ever saw. I couldn't have hit it with a paddle."

Meanwhile my good friend Bob Shaw was making spitball headlines. When Bob went to the Mets, the San Francisco writers joked that there wasn't anything wrong with his arm, he had merely run out of spit. And when Bob won five of his first six decisions with the Mets, opposing players and managers began screaming, and umpires began checking him out real good. He was delighted. "Did you read my clippings?" Bob called to me one day late in the season. I nodded. As Bob always said, you know how well your spitball's doing by the complaints you receive.

150

I got a little wet publicity of my own. My friend, Harry Jupiter, gave me a nice write-up in the San Francisco *Examiner*:

NEW YORK—*The Mets weren't complaining, mind you, they were just discussing Gaylord Perry's "sinkers."*

Gaylord calls 'em sinkers. The Mets call 'em spitters.

"I can't ever remember a game where a man threw as many spitballs as Perry threw tonight," said Whitey Herzog, the Mets' third base coach.

"I'll bet 75 percent of his pitches were spitters."

Not once, though, did the Mets ask plate umpire Billy Williams to inspect the baseballs Perry used in notching his sixteenth victory, an 11–1 job.

It's tough for the Mets to make much noise about spitters because they've got a couple of fellows who, it is rumored, occasionally wet 'em up.

Would you believe Jack Hamilton and Bob Shaw?

Everywhere the Giants go these days, there are winks and behind-the-hand remarks about the secret of Gaylord's sensational success this season.

Perry shakes his head. He says the secret is his hard slider, which sometimes sinks.

There are lots of spitters thrown in the National League. Since the rules prohibit the pitch, few players would be willing to acknowledge throwing spitters.

There are pitchers who throw 'em and get clobbered.

So trying to explain Perry's success by pointing to the spitball is patently unfair.

He's throwing the ball hard, keeping it low, and winning. Boy, is he winning!

And nobody's caught him breaking any rules.

Reporters tried to get him to confess last night, but he wouldn't.

151

"You know I don't throw a spitter," Gaylord said.
"Why would you want me to say that I do?"
And with that he headed for the showers.

After I beat Houston, 1–0, for my eighteenth victory, Astro outfielder Dave Nicholson said, "Does Perry throw a spitter? Everybody on the field knows he does. If it's a slider, it's an irrigated one."

I won my twentieth on August 20, ahead of every pitcher in either league. It was a five-hit 5–1 victory over Atlanta and over Tony Cloninger, who grew up in North Carolina the same time I did, who got $100,000 from the Braves a few days before I signed with the Giants and who went into the 1966 season with 67 big-league victories to my 24. What's more, in July he had beat us, 17–3, and had hit two grand-slam home runs. He was the first man in the history of the National League to hit two grand slams in one game. (By 1973, we were both in Cleveland— me with the Indians and Tony playing third base for the Howard Furniture Co. of North Carolina in the national slow-pitch softball tournament.) For several years, some people inside the Giant organization had been suspecting that maybe they'd signed the wrong prospect, that they should've bid a little higher and gotten Cloninger instead of Perry. I couldn't blame them for thinking like that; Tony had outpitched me from 1958 through 1965. But from 1966 on, it was my turn.

My spitter was getting better and better—and I was having a lot of fun with it. Sometimes, trying to hold a runner on first, I'd throw a wet one over to Cepeda. He'd give me a big know-it-all grin. Leo Durocher was managing the Cubs, and I loved to irritate him. He'd have the umpires look at the ball a dozen times. Each time I'd roll the ball to the umpire, whether I had anything on it or not. Durocher called me every name he could think of, and he sure could think of some honeys.

I sometimes chewed bubble gum and elm bark to get

152

the right kind of juice to last me through a game. One night I was on first base and was bunted to second. Dick Groat, playing shortstop, tagged me, hard. I went flying over backward and swallowed my gum and bark.

I looked up, panicked. "I . . . I swallowed my gum!" I said.

"That," said Groat, "ought to take care of your sinker."

The word was getting around good. Henry Aaron called me the best spitball pitcher he had ever faced. "He throws it harder than most pitchers and he has great control," said Henry. "Comes in like a knuckler but harder."

And Joe Torre, then a catcher, added, "I don't envy Tom Haller. The spitter is harder to catch than a knuckler when you throw it like Perry does."

Atlanta's pitching coach, Whit Wyatt, said, "Perry may be the greatest spitball pitcher since Burleigh Grimes. Whatever Gaylord calls it, hard slider or what, he is the toughest pitcher in the National League right now."

The nice thing is that none of these remarks were made unkindly. Nobody accused me of cheating. Ballplayers don't think a good spitballer is a criminal. They think he's an artist.

Everyone was praising the daylights out of me. Some people thought I might be the first pitcher to win 30 games since Dizzy Dean of the 1934 Cardinals. Others called me the prime prospect to win the Cy Young Pitcher of the Year Award in the National League.

But in September, I fell into an unbelievable slump.

I lost six straight games. I went from 20–2 to 20–8. Part of the explanation was I wasn't getting much batting support. But part of the fault was definitely mine.

In late September, Herman Franks told me to take a night off and visit Larry Jansen, who'd suffered a heart attack just before my twentieth victory. While convalescing, Jansen had seen me pitching on television. He had detected flaws in my delivery and timing. The day after I visited Larry, I pitched against the Phillies. In eight innings, the Phillies hit only four balls out of the infield. One of those four was a first-inning homer by Richie Allen and it cost me the game. Allen said afterward, "I wanted to get him before he got me too wet to swing." Despite the defeat I knew I'd straightened myself out.

One good thing about my hot streak coming to an end was getting off a diet of baked chicken. My favorite meal is steak, but Blanche had baked chicken for me in early May before I shut out the Cardinals, and from then on, it was chicken every workday. In the dugout before each game, I grabbed the bat rack and gave it a good shake— to put the whammy on enemy bats. I ran out to the mound every inning and when I had to make a key pitch, I'd turn my back to the plate and tap my right shoulder. The slump ended most of that superstitious stuff. Of course, I still wet up my fingers, just for good luck.

I finally won my twenty-first in Atlanta, with my friend Booger Scales and my folks cheering me on. The season came down to the final day, with us needing a victory plus a Dodger defeat to maybe force a tie and a play-off. We got our victory, but Sandy Koufax eliminated the second possibility. Sandy won his twenty-seventh game and led the league in strike-outs and in earned run average. Naturally, he got the Cy Young Award. I couldn't feel too bad about not getting the award; my teammate, Juan Marichal, didn't get it, either, and he won twenty-five that year.

At the end of the season, I flew to Phoenix where Dr. Harry Bonnell performed an operation to remove a calcium spur from my right instep. I had pitched the whole year with an aching left ankle and a bruised right instep, and judging from my statistics, I should've pitched my whole life like that.

The Giants took my mind off my sore feet by giving me a nice fat $15,000 raise. I was up to $35,000 a year. Everything was beautiful. My only regret was that so far in my career, not a single umpire had actually stopped a game to complain about my super-sinker.

That would come.

14

In 1967, the code of silence collapsed. Everybody began talking out loud about the spitter. I could hardly believe my ears.

For instance, Grady Hatton, the manager of the Astros, said he told one of his pitchers, Bob Bruce, to ask Phil Regan of the Cubs how to throw a spitter. "They were teammates in Detroit," said Hatton. "Bob came back with a pretty good spitball."

Regan himself wasn't exactly subtle. "I can't come right out and tell you I throw a spitter," he said. "But I don't use it nearly as much as everyone thinks." Leo Durocher, who was managing the Cubs, stopped yelling so much about other people's spitters.

Manager Eddie Stanky of the White Sox said other managers were instructing their pitching coaches to teach the spitter because the umpires weren't going to stop the pitch.

When I pitched against the Phillies, Gene Mauch would station himself at third base and scream, "Here it comes! Here it comes! Here it comes!" His batters were more startled by his screams than I was. Besides, Mauch was right only about half the time.

When Cleveland manager Joe Adcock asked umpire Larry Napp to check out Minnesota's Dean Chance, Early Wynn, the Twins' pitching coach, growled, "Adcock's got some nerve. There are three guys on his club who go out to the mound with a bucket of water and a sponge." Washington manager Gil Hodges was so upset by California pitcher Jack Hamilton, he wrote a five-page letter to Joe Cronin, the American League president. Hodges called Hamilton's spitter "the most flagrant I ever saw. . . ." Cronin supposedly replied, "Thanks for the note. I appreciate your frustration."

Cronin, incidentally, came out for legalization of the spitter; the National League president, Warren Giles, came out against it. "The fans enjoy offense," said Giles. "We don't catch all the murderers, but we don't legalize murder because of that." I don't think it was very nice of Mr. Giles to compare me, and my fellow spitballers, to murderers. We were more like con men, I think.

The reason the spitter got so much attention in 1967 was that the previous winter, the rules committee issued a statement saying, "There is no definite proof that the spitball is being used."

That opened the "floodgates," so to speak. Very few of us suspected we were enjoying the last year of the pure spitter.

Come to think of it, I didn't enjoy it too much. Bad luck hung like a cloud over my head. I shut out Atlanta in our home opener, then waited six weeks to win again. Statistically, I had a super year: I increased my complete games (18), innings pitched (293) and strike-outs (230) and reduced my earned run average (2.61). But my won-loss record was only 15–17, and they pay you to win.

Bob Stevens of the San Francisco *Chronicle* wrote: "It appears that Perry is snakebit," and a good example of my snakebite was my record against the St. Louis Cardinals. I lost to them five straight times—2–1, 2–1, 3–1, 4–1 and 2–0. My former teammate, Orlando Cepeda, traded to the Cardinals that year, beat me with home runs three times. "He threw me at least seven spitters today," Cepeda said after one game. "It's funny. Gaylord doesn't need the spitter. He has such good stuff. A spitter is for people who don't have anything. The thing I can't believe is he was throwing spitters to Dick Hughes." Hughes, a pitcher, said, "I'll tell you one thing, I don't throw the wet one. I tried, but I can't do it. At bat, I couldn't hit Gaylord with a boat paddle. More power to him. You use everything at your command. I wish I had a wet one." Hughes, by the way, threw a pretty good spitter.

The St. Louis Cardinals' manager Red Schoendienst said, "Perry throws the spitter about 85 percent of the time and there's nothing you can do about it. He goes to his mouth and he's supposed to wipe off his fingers afterwards. He doesn't wipe. The only way you can stop the spitter is to keep the pitcher from going to his mouth."

I told the writers, "What the Cards say doesn't bother me. They're talking about my hard slider." I never believed in bragging about the spitter.

After the All-Star break, I pitched as well as I ever have. I won 10 of my last 17 decisions, with a 1.71 ERA. On Labor Day, I pitched 16 scoreless innings against Cincinnati, stretching my scoreless-inning streak to 25.

My next start, I shut out Houston and extended my string to 34 innings. Tom Haller renamed my spitter a super-sinker. He kept telling the writers, "Gaylord's best pitch is his super-sinker."

My shutout string attracted a lot of attention. Somebody checked the record books and discovered that Walter

157

Johnson had pitched 56 consecutive shutout innings for the major-league record, and that the Giants' Carl Hubbell held the National League mark with 46⅓ scoreless innings. I was only a dozen innings away from tying Hubbell's record.

My next start was against the Cubs. I extended my scoreless string to 40, just 6⅓ innings from the record. Then, in the seventh, I walked lead-off batter Ron Santo. Ernie Bank came up and topped one of my spitters right back to me. It should've been an easy doubleplay, but I threw the ball into center field. Santo went to third and Banks stopped at first base.

Leo Durocher broke up laughing at me. "You didn't wipe off," he hollered. "You threw a spitter to second base!"

I didn't think it was very funny, especially when Bob Raudman grounded into a doubleplay, allowing Santo to score an unearned run and ruin my record. I had nobody to blame but myself. I went on to pitch five more shutout innings after that, but who cared?

Durocher had helped make 1967 a big spitball year. The previous season, he had held up so many games so many times demanding pitchers and baseballs be checked that a directive was issued to speed up the game. Umpires had orders to limit the number of time-outs they called. Hitters were not allowed to call for the ball so often for inspection, and they were ordered to stay in the batter's box once they got in it.

The directives to speed up the game helped a spitballer. It cut down on the times a ball could be thrown out of the game, so we could keep a soiled ball in the game longer. (Herman Franks ordered us to make sure when the Giants came to bat we got rid of the old ball some way or other so our guys would have a new one to hit.)

Despite all this, I still lost 17 games—ten of them by one run, five of those ten by 2–1 scores.

But one thing made the Perry world a lot brighter. My only son, Jack, was born on August 22, 1967. The papers quoted me saying, "Blanche came through." Jack was our first son after three daughters. When he was born, the doctors told us, "You've got a son, but he'll never pitch." Jack's right arm was damaged at birth. With hard work he straightened his arm. Now he can throw and bat better than most youngsters.

At the end of the season, the Giants gave me a $10,000 raise, boosting my salary to an even $45,000. I thought I deserved another $5,000 but Mr. Stoneham had been generous to the Perrys when we were hit by that tax case. So I didn't argue.

But the big news of that year was to come. The story broke in November out of the baseball winter meetings:

> *The Rules committee voted to abolish once again the spitball (already deemed illegal), beginning with the opening game in 1968. A pitcher no longer will be able to bring his pitching hand in contact with his mouth or lips, and if he ignores the rule he'll be warned once by the umpire and will be thrown out of the game immediately upon detection of a second violation.*

The story went on to name pitchers accused of throwing the spitters: Cal Koonce of the Mets, Jim Lonborg of the Red Sox, Dick Hughes of the Cardinals, Jack Hamilton of the Angels, Larry Sherry of the Astros, Don Drysdale of the Dodgers, Ronnie Kline of the Twins, Dick Farrell of the Phillies, and me.

That rule virtually ended the pure spitball in baseball. I had the whole winter and spring to work out an adjustment. It wasn't easy.

15

Rule 8.02—*The pitcher shall not (a) (1) Bring his pitching hand in contact with his mouth or lips while in the 18-foot circle surrounding the pitching rubber.* PENALTY: *For violation of this part of this rule the umpire shall immediately call a ball.*

This was the rule baseball finally settled upon in 1968, after a spring training full of confusion. Chicago White Sox pitching coach Johnny Sain is annoyed about that change to this day. He told me, "I don't think it's fair to have that rule on the books. A pitcher needs to wet his fingers. Not to throw a slip pitch, but to get a better grip on the ball. What do you do when you have trouble turning a page of a book? You wet your finger and it clings. The same thing is true when you mix saliva and rosin. Why penalize all the pitchers because a handful throw a slip pitch?"

So for the 1968 season I had the task of unlearning a learned procedure of "cap-to-mouth-to-wipe" and learning to transfer a slicky substance hidden on my skin or uniform to my fingers. That winter I settled on my decoys and practiced them every night at home. The kids thought I was a deaf-mute learning sign language. I tried to be philosophical about it all. Gosh, grease was a little more sanitary. It was soothing for sunburn and nicks from shaving and it did wonders for my hands. They went from dishpan to the skin-you-love-to-touch. I figured all the other spitballers were going through the same thing that winter. All but Phil Regan, that is. He had been using grease all along. I guess, in a way, you could say "The Vulture" was ahead of his time.

I began working out right after the Christmas holidays. I ran for almost a month before I began to throw. I had to have my body in top condition for all the experimenting that was ahead. Blanche didn't know it, but she was the first person to catch my greaser. I tossed easily to her at our home in San Mateo several times a week. I didn't want to make a big thing about it with her. I didn't want her to know I was a little concerned about my ability to make the switch.

I was met by another blow that spring. The Giants traded Haller to the Dodgers for second baseman Ron Hunt. Haller had worked with me on the spitter and I was relying on his receiving to help me make the switch. The Giants had catchers Dick Dietz, Jack Hyatt and newcomer Bob Barton. They had to learn my strengths and weaknesses. Herman knew of my dilemma and had Dietz catch every time I was pitching—on the sidelines, in batting practice and in every exhibition game possible. Dietz was something, a real zany. He was having the time of his life that spring. He kept giving me THE SIGN. While I was serious and concerned, he was calling me "Greaser."

161

I found out that the grease ball worked about the same as the spitball, except it was more consistent. It had a more delicate feel to it, like the difference between power steering in your car and the conventional steering. I found that the less I applied to the ball the more control I had.

I had the worst spring of my career, not surprisingly. The two previous springs I had an 8–0 record and ERA of less than 3.00. Now everybody was watching to see how I'd adjust. Herman kept telling reporters, "Nothing counts until the bell rings. Gaylord looks all right to me. He looks the same to me." Yes, I still had two legs, a head and two arms. But I sure wasn't the same.

Herman held me out of the early exhibition games, but finally I faced the Cleveland Indians and gave up four runs in five innings. Maybe the spring training headlines tell the story of my struggle from spit to grease much better than I can:

"HAS SPITBALL RULE HURT PERRY?. . . He has pitched 13 innings, allowed 11 runs, all earned, 21 hits have rattled off his pitches, 12 of them when the Chicago Cubs trounced the Giants here yesterday, 10–4."—March 21, San Francisco *Examiner*.

"PERRY CAN'T FIND PLATE, GIANTS' BIG PROBLEM. . . Going into the final exhibitions of the spring and scheduled for one more start, Perry is 1–3 in Cactus League competition and 8.38 in the earned run average books. This is not what you'd call impressive."—April 2, San Francisco *Chronicle*.

Herman was walking around with that "don't let me down" look. He told the press, "It's nothing permanent or even anything to get excited about. Perry's working on a few new things and he's just been a little off target. His arm is strong and he's healthy."

I sure was working on "a few new things" and they all were slippery. And I sure was beginning to worry. I struggled until the final day in an exhibition game with the Mets in Phoenix. I gave up five runs in the first two innings. Then, finally, it all came together. I retired 14 of the next 15 Mets, nine in a row. A big grin spread over Herman's face. I had made the switch. I finished training with a 1–4 record and a 7.75 earned run average. Before opening day, a San Francisco paper carried a large two-paneled photograph of me going to my mouth with my fingers. It read, "Watch it, Gaylord!"

I knew I was back in the groove after my first regular season start. I got no batting support and lost to Pittsburgh, 2–1. Willie Stargell laughed when he saw my dipsy-do with the grease treatment. "I see you're keeping up with the times," he yelled to me. Word spread fast that I was still in business.

Early that May, Philadelphia relief pitcher John Boozer was thrown out of the New York–Philadelphia game in the seventh inning for going to his mouth while warming up. Plate umpire Ed Vargo, seeing Boozer go to his mouth three times, ejected him and ruled that the first batter of the inning, Bud Harrelson, would come to the plate with a three-ball, no-strike count. Vargo also ruled that if Boozer's replacement, Dick Hall, went to his mouth only once the game would be forfeited to the Mets. Hall pitched two strikes to Harrelson and then got him to ground out. Warren Giles stepped into that mess the next day, telling his five umpire crew chiefs that the anti-spitter rule did not apply while warming up.

It took baseball until June to realize that it had successfully wiped dry the spitball only to launch a new era—the grease ball era. After Drysdale blanked me, 3–0, to register his record fifth consecutive shutout early that season, Herman hit the roof.

"Every one of the Dodger starting pitchers is throwing a Vaseline ball—Don Drysdale, Bill Singer and Don Sutton. The only difference between Drysdale and the other two is that Drysdale throws harder so his Vaseline ball breaks more. He's thrown a spitter for years and knows how to handle stuff on the ball. Vaseline, spit—what's the difference? They've taken the spitter from the pitcher and given him the Vaseline ball. I've never seen so many guys with Vaseline in their hair—just plastered down. [Well, that left me out!] I've seen caps sopped with Vaseline."

My first grease check came in Philadelphia later that month. Umpire Bob Engle came out at the request of manager Bob Skinner and felt my ears. Now you have to admit that standing in the center of the diamond in front of 22,000 fans and having somebody tweeking your ear-lobes is a little embarrassing. I felt a little stupid but that is just one of the hazards of the trade.

Things were pretty quiet until the end of July when Durocher took after me again. Somewhere in the middle of a two-hit, 4–1 victory over the Cubs, Durocher stomped out to plate umpire Vargo.

"Ed, don't you notice anything unusual about Perry's pitches?" Durocher demanded.

"I do not."

"Well, that ain't the law of gravity that's making that ball dip."

"Perry's throwing his sinker, Leo."

"Inspect his cap and head."

Vargo came out and took off my cap and felt the tip and inspected the lining.

"What you expect to pull outta the hat, a rabbit or something?" I asked, trying to lighten the seriousness of the moment. He checked my hair, and then the back of my neck.

"Hmmm," he said, "Gaylord, you need a hair cut."

"You know a good barber in Chicago?"

"Try the hotel."

"I'm gonna get me one of them Beatle cuts."

"Forget it, you don't have a chance," said Vargo, bumping me lightly on the chest with his fist. "But you could sure use a shave."

All the time Leo was smiling over by the dugout thinking I'm catching it pretty good from Vargo. The fans

164

in Wrigley Field were booing and cheering the umpire who they thought was threatening to throw me out. About 90 percent of the time a visit from the umpire is merely a social engagement, a way for the umpire to get the opposing manager off his back.

My first surprise inspection was by first base umpire Al Barlick. I had served up two straight dipsy-doodles to Tony Taylor of the Phillies. I had my back turned to first while waiting for Dietz to toss back the ball, when suddenly my cap jerked off my head. I was used to the wind doing that in Candlestick. But this was Barlick who yanked off my lid. He then inspected my glove. "I can't find a thing," said Barlick. I said, "Tell me what you're looking for and maybe I can help you." He just smiled and said, "Questionable material," and ran back to his position. For some reason the umpires always checked my glove. I never put anything on the glove. It would be too easy to detect. But after you got up a good sweat you could put a little something on the cap and it'd all blend together.

Late that season I learned the importance of keeping a clean uniform, not only for sanitary reasons but to avoid suspicion. In a nationally televised game out of St. Louis, manager Red Schoendienst protested a stain on my pants to plate umpire—yes, again—Vargo and out he came.

"Perry, Red doesn't like the looks of that stain on your trousers. He thinks you're getting *it* from there. Let me check it." There had been a soiled spot from the day before. It was about 95 degrees and my perspiration made the spot spread.

"I can't feel anything," Vargo admitted, "but how about changing your pants anyway?" "Right here?" I asked.

I went into the clubhouse while the TV world waited. The fans got a little mad about the delay. But at least they learned how long it takes a player to change his baseball britches. I put a little gob of something on my pants because I knew after that delay Vargo was not gonna come out again no matter what my drop did. I was right. I beat the Cards, 4–1. I caught a look at Schoendienst staring at me with his hands on his hips. Finally, he raised both hands over his head and brought them down in a helpless gesture of disgust. He couldn't say a word and he knew it.

The most significant grease ball incident that season involved not me but Phil Regan, then of the Cubs, in a game against Cincinnati. Chris Pelekoudas, who was working home plate, charged Regan with throwing three illegal pitches. Pelekoudas said he determined the pitches were illegal by seeing the "abnormal" flight of the ball. It was an unprecedented action by an umpire and scared the daylights out of all pitchers. (It could be a common action in 1974, with the new rule.) Here's what happened:

Regan came in to pitch in the seventh inning. The furor erupted after the count had reached one ball, two strikes on pinch hitter Mack Jones of the Reds, the first hitter Regan faced. Pelekoudas had warned Regan when he reached the mound. "I don't want to see you throw any illegal pitches, Regan." When Pelekoudas saw what he considered an illegal pitch, he called it a ball, instead of ejecting Regan from the game as he could have.

Durocher argued violently and was ejected, as was coach Al Spangler. The count was ruled 2–2 when Jones flied to center, but Pelekoudas disallowed the play and called another illegal pitch, making the count 3–2. Then Jones grounded out. Everything returned to normal until the ninth when Regan struck out Pete Rose on a 2–2 pitch. Pelekoudas called it an illegal pitch. Rose, who was walking back to the dugout, was ordered back to the plate. Rose singled on the next pitch. Catcher Randy Hundley argued and was thrown out.

Pelekoudas was quoted after the game as saying: "The umpires as a team had discussed this thing about Regan before the game and decided to bring it to a head. Regan defied me. I warned him, and at first I decided to throw him out of the game when he threw the next Vaseline ball. Then I had second thoughts. I said, To hell with him,

166

let him stay in the game and suffer. Every illegal pitch will be a ball.

"I'll admit it's the first time I can ever remember an illegal pitch being charged. We've gone out and warned a pitcher before and they've always stopped throwing it. Regan didn't deny he threw it. He just kept saying, 'Find it.'"

The Cubs demanded an investigation by Giles. The Cubs' vice president John Holland called it the "worst umpiring I've seen in the history of the major leagues." He added, "The umpire should throw the pitcher out of the game, not call everything a ball and give them an extra dozen outs. Leo could have protested but it would have been the most ridiculous protest in the world, trying to argue that your own pitcher should be thrown out of the game. After all, the umpires, in effect, have called Phil Regan a cheater. That's a serious charge anytime and even more serious when you consider the man is a preacher." (Regan occasionally gave talks on religion before boys' clubs and religious groups.)

Pelekoudas, an umpire for 20 seasons, said, "I've been umpiring long enough to know an illegal pitch when I see one. We're not stupid. We can spot an illegal pitch."

Giles rushed to Chicago and met with Regan and Durocher and Holland. According to the reports of that meeting, Giles asked Regan if he was throwing a Vaseline ball and Regan, of course, said he was not. Giles apologized to Regan and indicated that thereafter no umpire crew should make judgment rulings on illegal pitches unless they found distinct evidence that a foreign substance had been applied to the ball.

Giles in effect turned his back on his umpires. One disgusted umpire told me right after that, "From now on, I don't care if you have a bucket of water and a lube rack to dip the ball in, I'm not gonna call anything." (The funny thing is that later the same season, Regan was in a home-plate collision in a game Pelekoudas was

167

umpiring. When Regan arose, I hear, he left a tube of Vaseline and two slippery elm tablets in the dust.)

The next time Regan and Pelekoudas faced each other, Pelekoudas said he counted 14 illegal pitches in the first inning Regan worked. "I didn't call them because we have no physical evidence. I'm not the boss and I have to abide by what Mr. Giles rules." Regan played the sympathy bit beautifully. He expressed concern for how the situation might affect baseball and his family. He said, "I have a twelve-year-old daughter at home who is quite upset and worried about this. And then there are the kids in the stands who keep yelling at me 'Where do you keep your Vaseline?' That isn't good for baseball." (I couldn't have put it better myself. Sniff. Sniff.)

From then on, however, Mr. Giles himself was on the lookout for the grease-ballers. Once he approached Herman about my pitching. The two had a meeting in Cincinnati, I found out later.

Herman said, "Now look, Mr. Giles. Gaylord is not throwing that pitch. My pitcher is not throwing that grease ball."

Giles said, "All right. But I'll be out there watching myself the next time he pitches."

I knew of none of that conversation. The next time out I didn't have my good stuff. My fast ball wasn't moving. My slider wasn't sharp. So I had to go to it. Giles was in the stands. Herman was over in the dugout just shaking his head, cussing a blue streak. After the game he came to me and said, "You really got me in trouble now."

"What do you mean?" I asked.

"Two days ago I have a meeting with Giles and I tell him you aren't throwing that pitch. I swear on a stack of Bibles you are clean. And you weren't throwing it."

"That's right," I agreed.

"And tonight, that's all you threw!"

"Well, Herman, I didn't have my good slider. I didn't have my good fast ball. What do you want me to do?"

He turned around and walked off shaking his head—and grinning.

How do you tell about a no-hitter? How do you describe the pressure? The luck it takes? Here's how the late-great Giants broadcaster Russ Hodges described my final inning against the Cardinals on radio station KSFO San Francisco:

"Well, to try to do this job, Gaylord Perry has to wade through three great hitters, Lou Brock and Bobby Tolan and Curt Flood. And remember, the Cardinals are still trying to win this ball game. They are only 1–0 behind, so, if one of them bunts, it will not be unsportsmanlike. . . .

"Perry throws, Brock swings and misses for strike one. Only Marichal has been able to do this in the history of the San Francisco Giants. Now Brock, trying to get Perry out of the groove, steps out. Now Brock steps in again. Perry winds, comes in with the pitch, Brock swings and bounds it to Lanier who's up with it, throws to first, they got him! Perry's two outs away.

"Bobby Tolan has struck out, grounded out twice. Willie McCovey made a great play to get him the last time up. The Giant outfield is not as deep for Tolan as they were for Brock, but the infielders are in a bit tighter because Bobby is an accomplished bunter. Tolan backing out. . . . He is also trying to get Perry out of the rhythm out there. And here's the windup and the pitch to Tolan—a take low for ball one.

"One down top of the ninth, Gaylord Perry two outs away from the game in the record book in big bold type. . . . Perry throws to the plate, Tolan runs up to bunt. He misses it and it's a strike and it's one and one. Ball and a strike to Bobby Tolan. . . . The pitch, swung on, grounder to Ron Hunt, he's got it, he throws to first, out number two!

"And the Cardinals' leading hitter, Curt Flood, is up

at the plate. Anybody nervous? Anybody excited? We are! Flood has grounded out, popped to second and popped to first. Dick Dietz gives the sign to Gaylord, who throws to Flood and there's a take for a called strike. Oh-and-one the count to number 21, Curt Flood. And here's Gaylord Perry winding, he throws to the plate, Flood takes strike two called. Candlestick Park is in a frenzy. And Perry winds. He throws to Flood. Outside for a ball. One ball and two strikes. If Gaylord is excited you certainly can't see it. . . . Perry to the windup, delivers to Curt Flood. Swung on, fouled off, he's still alive.

"It's one and two, to number 21, Curt Flood. Perry tugs at the peak of the cap. Now the windup and the pitch to Flood. Strike three called! IT'S A NO-HITTER FOR GAYLORD PERRY!"

When I think of Bobby Feller pitching 12 one-hitters and only two no-hitters in a lifetime, I know how precious that ball game was. It was the second no-hitter against the Cardinals in 49 years. I was greasing that night, but only a few times. My super drop could sneak through the infield as well as not, and with the speedy Cardinals' running and bunting game, I sure wasn't going to make it easy for them, especially in that final inning. In fact, with a little more luck, I might have pitched a perfect game as fellow North Carolinian Catfish Hunter did across the Bay in Oakland. But I gave up a two-out second-inning walk to Mike Shannon and a two-out eighth-inning walk to Phil Gagliano. I struck out nine Cardinals. I had a great slider that day. Honest.

What did that game mean to me? Well, I took three sleeping pills and didn't close my eyes all night. I called Mom and Daddy. They didn't hear the game through the St. Louis station because they thought I was scheduled for the following night. But George Griffin called them from Griffin's Quick Lunch. There was a whole gang gathering as the game went on. They ate Brunswick Stew on the house to celebrate.

Jansen kidded me before the game: "If you shut 'em out, you might get a draw with Bob Gibson." He called it. Gibson was great, too, fanning ten and giving up only four hits. I also owe part of it to Hunt, who scored the only run with a first-inning home run. His only other home run that season was back in May.

The Giants presented me with a $1000 check for my no-hitter and gave Dietz $100. I read about pitchers getting some real good commercial endorsements for no-hitters. I didn't have long to wait. A public relations man from an ice cream and milk company wanted me to pose for a picture they would put up on billboards all over San Francisco saying how much I like their products. It was an offer I *could* refuse. For my picture they were willing to give me and my family all the ice cream and milk we could eat—at cost—which meant I could buy a gallon of ice cream from them for 39 cents. Heck, Smokie the Bear must get more than that posing for forest fires.

That wasn't the end to the no-hit story at Candlestick because Ray Washburn pitched one against us the very next day. The Cardinal pitcher walked five and fanned eight for the first back-to-back no-hitters recorded in the 92-year history of the major leagues.

For me it was another good season from an artistic standpoint but not in the won-loss column. I finished up with a 16–15 won-loss record, losing three by 2–0 scores, four by 2–1 counts and four by 3–1 scores. Marichal won 26 to my 16, yet his earned run average was 2.44 and mine was 2.43.

The no-hitter was great. But I was also very proud of the one-hitter I pitched that season, because I got great satisfaction out of the way I conquered my emotions. There were four errors behind me in that game, I think, maybe five, and ordinarily that would have upset me. But

171

I kept control of myself and my "stuff" and pitched a fine game.

It was a busy winter for me but for the first time I could stop worrying about making the club, getting into the starting rotation, learning the wet one, conquering my immaturity on the mound and then mastering the grease ball. It was a great winter with the family. I even got on TV, doing a hunting film with Bing Crosby, but I learned that I had little chance for a movie acting career. I didn't talk plain enough and hair is "in" which leaves me out.

That season was good for a raise to $60,000. I wanted another $5000 but Feeney, who nearly ruined me with his rules committee, said that my salary was getting high and had to be leveled out. It was all right with me. I figured I'd keep doing better financially as long as my super-sinker didn't "level out."

16

If [the umpire is] convinced there has been a foreign substance applied to the ball, the pitcher shall immediately be removed from the game. If the above ruling does not control or eliminate the illegal practice of applying a foreign substance to a ball, a more severe penalty will be necessary. The enforcement of this is strictly an act of judgment on the part of the umpire and is not subject to argument or protest.

Warren Giles, the National League president, issued this edict in June of 1969. Ironically, in the two previous All-Star games, the pitchers were me and Don Drysdale. Giles hugged me after my victory. I don't think he got anything greasy on his suit. Maybe Don stained Giles' suit; maybe that got him upset.

I couldn't really blame Giles. He was roughly treated in the sports pages on the Regan incident in 1968, and in 1969 the papers kept making a big thing out of complaints about the greaser. Early in May, Jim Maloney of the Reds fired a no-hitter against Houston. The Astros' manager, Harry Walker, didn't like it.

"Maloney did it with a grease ball," Walker said. "If he throws that thing as well as he did last night, he'll get another no-hitter before the season is out. You know he throws it, I know he throws it, and the umpires know he throws it."

Maloney replied, "He can say whatever he wants to say. I'm out there to beat him and he's out there trying to beat me." Spoken like a true member of The Brotherhood.

The next night, Don Wilson of the Astros came right back and no-hit the Reds, matching the back-to-back feat that Washburn and I accomplished the year before. Cincinnati manager Dave Bristol didn't accuse Wilson of greasing up. He just said, "I'm not a Don Wilson fan. I don't think many of our guys think much of Wilson, either."

A few days later, the late Gil Hodges, then the manager of the Mets, had a quiet five-minute chat about me with the home-plate umpire. Hodges produced a baseball he said contained "a jelly substance on it." I couldn't have had anything to do with that; I don't even like jam.

All the little things helped cause Giles' edict. It had a quick impact.

Two days after Giles' statement, we played the Mets in Candlestick. Before the game, umpire-in-chief Doug Harvey came out to warn me, "If I find anything on you, Gaylord, I'll have to wipe you off. If I find it again on you or the ball, you're gone!"

"You got nothing to worry about, Doug," I assured him.

In the first inning, Harvey threw out a couple of baseballs. With Tommie Agee at bat, Harvey leaned over until his lips were almost nibbling catcher Jack Hiatt's ear.

"I want to see this next ball after you catch it," Harvey whispered. The ball zoomed in and the bottom dropped out of it.

"That's it!" yelled Harvey, "I want that ball!" Hiatt, pretending not to hear, started his quick throw back to me. Harvey grabbed Jack's arm just as he was releasing his throw and the ball rolled down the third-base line. Hiatt and Harvey both started for the ball, stumbled and fell in a tangled heap at the plate. They struggled to their knees and half crawled to the ball. By that time, the ball had trickled 15 feet in the cleansing dust. When Harvey picked it up, he didn't find any incriminating evidence.

Harvey and his crew converged and checked my uniform and took my cap, but they found nothing. I knew they wouldn't. From the third inning on, I was left alone.

Unfortunately, Harvey injured Hiatt's throwing arm. Feeny protested to Giles that Hiatt could have been seriously injured and that Harvey's procedure was ill-advised. Giles agreed. Our new manager was understanding. "Harvey had a job to do," said Clyde King. "He apologized to Jack and me. All I told him was that whatever he was looking for, he wasn't going to find it by putting one of my players on the disabled list."

No umpire has injured me yet, but I've learned to put up with a lot. It was Ed Sudol, I think, who once decided I had some gooey stuff underneath the blouse in my pants. Actually, my socks were slipping that day and I kept reaching down to pull them up. The batters must've thought I was getting something from down there. So I played it to the hilt, going to my pants and throwing natural sliders and curves and they were swinging for greasers. Sudol came out to the mound and wanted to see my pants. He made me pull them up over my knees. The fans, who were cheering Sudol all the way, started whistling at me.

Orlando Pena used to get inspected a lot, too, and he told me once about an incident that happened when he

175

was pitching for Kansas City. Gil Hodges, then managing Washington, got a little suspicious and asked umpire Art Paparella to take a look at Pena.

"I'm not throwing spitters," Pena told the umpire. "I can't throw hard enough to make a spitter work. I try to throw one and it comes out a slow ball. My spitter's so slow, I could hit it. And I have a policy of never throwing a pitch *I* could hit."

"What are you throwing?" Paparella asked.

"A Cuban fork ball," Pena said. "With something extra."

Paparella began pulling out Pena's shirt and looking under his arms. Pena started giggling.

"What's so funny?" said Paparella.

"I can't help it," said Pena. "I'm ticklish."

At the very end of June, for the first time since Giles' edict, the Pelekoudas crew got assigned to a Giant series —against Cincinnati. I guess Chris couldn't wait to see me. In the third inning, on a 2–2 pitch to Pete Rose, Pelekoudas suddenly shouted, "Hold it! Hold it right there."

He threw the ball out of the game. He said the last pitch had dipped suspiciously. Then he came toward me with a cloth in his hand.

"What's up, Chris?" I asked.

"Wipe, Gaylord, wipe. Your face, head and back of your neck."

"No soap with the towel?"

I thought that was a pretty funny line, but Pelekoudas didn't laugh. Neither did my manager. King was furious with Pelekoudas. "Pelekoudas told me no one was complaining, he was doing it on his own," said Clyde. "And he told me that if Perry went to the back of his neck again, he was out of the game. It's persecution." I suppose I should've been angry with Rose for getting me in trouble, but I got him in trouble with a different umpiring crew. He was protesting one of my sinkers, and the umpire thought he heard Pete say a bad word. He threw Pete out of the game. Pete was literally carried off the field—he wanted to get at the ump—and that day, as a part of a giveaway program, the Reds players had tossed 1500 rubber balls into the stands, souvenirs for fans. When Rose was ejected, the fans threw 1500 rubber balls back on the field. It looked like a Walt Disney finale to me.

A week later, I got special treatment again, from Tom Gorman and his crew. I invited them to throw me out instead of the ball I threw. It was obvious harassment.

Suddenly, after a month or so, the harassment stopped. The writers kidded that I had come up with "a dry spitter," meaning I was going legit. I wasn't doing anything differently then than I was at the start of the season. I later learned that Chub Feeney had protested to Giles about the unfair treatment I was receiving.

It was a trying year—not only for me but for all pitchers. That year, they lowered the pitching mound from 15 to 10 inches, and reduced the strike zone from the knees and tops of the shoulders to above the knees and the armpits. They also juiced the ball; I mean made it livelier, not wet.

I know because I hit my first big-league homer that year, off Claude Osteen of the Dodgers, over the center-field fence in Candlestick Park. It's easy to remember because my home-run ball came down to earth the day lunar module Eagle touched down on the moon. (Alvin Dark had told a sportswriter three years earlier, "A man'll land on the moon before Gaylord will hit a home run in the big leagues." Dark was right—by 40 minutes.)

While my brother Jim was a 20-game winner for Minnesota, I won 19 games and had a 2.95 earned run average. They called me and Marichal the best one-two pitching punch in baseball. Only five pitchers in the league had averaged more than 15 victories for the past four seasons, a Giants' press release pointed out: Marichal (86), Bob

Gibson (76) of the Cardinals, Perry (71), Ferguson Jenkins (67) of the Cubs and Claude Osteen (66) of the Dodgers.

I waved Giant's publicist Art Santo Domingo's figures in front of Mr. Stoneham. He smiled. We never had a contract problem. He offered me a raise of $15,000. I wanted $80,000. We settled on a two-year deal of $75,000 each and I purchased a three-acre ranch home in Portola Valley.

One other big thing happened that year. Willie Mays hit his six hundredth homer. It took 18 years and went 391 feet. It made him the second man in baseball history to hit 600.

17

When Chub Feeney left the Giants to become president of the National League in 1970, Horace Stoneham lost a son-in-law, and I lost my protector. Feeney had talked to Giles the year before to get Pelekoudas off my back, but as president of the league, Chub couldn't go out of his way to help me. Everybody was wondering what his attitude was going to be, especially me. After all, Feeney knew me well. Very well.

My third pitch of the season, I found out what kind of year it was going to be. Plate umpire Shag Crawford came out to check my fingers. "Gaylord," Crawford said, "this is a new season and we're on orders not to put up with any shenanigans. Might as well get it straight now."

My next start, Tom Gorman began throwing out base-balls as if they were contaminated. You've heard of Tinkers to Evers to Chance. This was Perry to Dietz to Gorman to the ball bag—I could see it was really helping me a lot to have a friend in power.

Pelekoudas worked my third start. It was in the Astrodome, and Houson manager Harry Walker kept bugging Pelekoudas the whole game. Rookie umpire John Davidson was behind the plate when rookie John Mayberry came up in the fifth inning. He had hit a home run his first time up. This time, on a 1–1 count, I threw Mayberry a terrific sinker. It dipped a foot, and he missed it by a foot.

Pelekoudas, out at second, screamed to Davidson, "Get the ball, John. Get that ball from Dietz."

Davidson got the ball, and all four umpires marched to the mound. Each one was looking at me like I carried some mysterious germ.

"Here, what's this?" said Pelekoudas. He pointed at my lower right wrist.

"My lower right wrist," I said.

"Wipe that."

He claimed he saw grease. Why would I put grease there? Try to touch your right fingers to your lower right wrist. It's impossible. And the other hand is covered with a glove.

Pelekoudas said later, "Gaylord had stuff all over the lower part of his right arm." But he added, "Funny thing though, I couldn't find any of it on the baseball."

Walker bellowed from the dugout, "You're wasting your time. Dietz wiped the ball clean before you got it." (He knew so much. I wouldn't be surprised if Harry used to throw a spitter for fun.)

One umpire turned my glove inside out, another examined my belt, Davidson got my cap, and Pelekoudas went into the dugout and got a bunch of towels. I wiped my face, neck, arms and every other place Chris pointed.

"Don't forget behind the ears, Perry," he said in all seriousness.

"You ought to buy a Turkish bath and run it in the off season," I suggested.

After five or six minutes—an all-time search record—they were convinced I was legal. The game resumed and I struck out Mayberry on a pitch that sank a foot. Nobody found fault with me the rest of the game, especially Mayberry. He hit a three-run homer in the eighth, and I lost the game.

Asked after the game what he'd found, Pelekoudas replied, "A lubricant. Just say it was a lubricant."

Since the Regan incident Pelekoudas couldn't wipe me off; I had to wipe off myself. I must say I did a real professional job, from my own point of view.

The Pelekoudas crew greeted me a little later in Philadelphia. Before my first pitch, Chris told Clyde King, "Let us have no baby oil today. We aren't going to stand for anything. If I see the slightest hint of a grease ball, Perry's out of the game."

It was beginning to get ridiculous. I didn't mind being inspected sometimes, but not when I was throwing changeups. Pelekoudas denied he had a vendetta against me.

A few days later, in Cincinnati, Pelekoudas called a balk on our rookie pitcher, Jim Johnson. And a whole bunch of us were arguing and telling Chris what we thought of him. And who got the thumb? Right. "We are just doing our job," said Pelekoudas. "Personalities don't enter into it." He repeated that his crew wasn't out to "get Perry." That was the only time I've ever been ejected in the big leagues.

More and more, I got to feeling my old friend Chub Feeney wasn't my old friend any more. He was acting impartially, too impartially for my good.

Fred Fleig, the supervisor of National League umpires, said the umpires were not making an example of me. "What we're out to do this season," he said, "is see that as far as is reasonable, the game is played strictly accord-

181

ing to the rules. The umpires are not picking on Perry. Their job is to watch every pitcher and call every infraction as they see it."

I got to know all the umpires real good that May and June. They all kept coming out to the mound to visit me. I did whatever they asked, but they never found anything. Nobody should ever catch a grease-baller with the goods. You'd be surprised how much cleaning off a pitcher can do by the time the umpire walks 60 feet 6 inches to the mound. In an instant, you can wipe *the* spot. An alert catcher helps, too—one who can keep his eye and maybe his thumb right on the league president's signature.

For the second year in a row, the umpires let up on me after the first half of the season. I was hardly bothered again. Augie Donatelli gave me a quick once-over in September, the day I won my twentieth victory. That victory put the Perrys in the record books. Jim had defeated Oakland a few days earlier for his twenty-second victory. We were the first brothers ever to win 20 games apiece in the same season. The Deans never did it nor did the Coveleskies. Jim—who'd won 20 the year before—wound up 24–12 and won the Cy Young Award in the American League. I went 23–13, pitched four consecutive shutouts and finished second to Bob Gibson for the Cy Young Award in the National League. (That year, Jim and I became the first brothers ever to oppose each other in an All-Star game. Neither of us pitched great. I pitched the sixth and seventh innings for our side and gave up two runs; Jim pitched the seventh and eighth for his side and gave up one run. My side won in extra innings.)

Since the umpire always gets the last word in any argument, here's the last word on me from Pelekoudas, spoken during the 1973 season:

"I kept a close eye on Gaylord. I found evidence on him. Thing about Gaylord was when I found it on him, he would wipe off clean and he would stay clean. At least in my games. I found grease on his glove wrist, the back of his neck and on his forehead. I've caught Regan, Bob Moose of Pittsburgh, Don Sutton with grease on his wrist, Jim Bunning with pine tar on his glovehand. Bill Singer has one of the good grease balls in the game. But Gaylord's was the best I ever saw.

"In the Regan deal, Giles decided for Regan. He said he cleared him because Regan was a Christian man and he didn't think he would cheat. I told Giles, 'Well I'm a Christian man and I don't lie.' Mr. Giles said he could not perceive that a man could detect a grease ball because of the action of the ball in flight. (Which, of course, is exactly what the umpires were told to start perceiving in 1974.) A grease ball is thrown like a fast ball. You have to have a lot of velocity on it. But it comes in with no spin, then it sinks and breaks down. You detect that thing on sight. Heck, yes. Some call it a hard slider. Hard slider, my foot. A slider spins. A fork ball spins a little bit. The grease ball comes in dead.

"I saw Gaylord one time in Cincinnati with his hair full of grease. I warned him. 'If you touch that once, I'm going to climb all over you.' Well, he went the whole game and never touched there once. After the game, he had to cross the infield at Crosley Field to get to the dressing room. He called me over and handed me a cloth. I opened it up and there was a tube of Vaseline. I still have it. It's in a special place in my trophy case.

"It got so, Gaylord wouldn't throw that pitch when I was behind the plate. I said, 'Gaylord, if you're going to operate that way, I'm not going to be coming after you when I'm on the bases. Only when I'm behind the plate.' He said, 'That's fair enough.' It should be left up to the plate umpire. He can see the pitch. He should call it. But an umpire's life is a lot easier over here in the National League now that Perry and Singer are in the American League."

I think I helped quiet the umpires myself late in the

1970 season by picking up an old spitter trick I had almost forgotten. I began to use a resin bag almost every other pitch. I got myself in the habit of bouncing it in my hand from the back of my right hand, over the fingertips to the palm. It was for the umpires' benefit. They knew it was impossible to throw a grease ball with resin on the finger tips. Right?

In 1970, I did add the fork ball to my arsenal. I had been working on it for over a season. It dipped like a grease ball, but slightly off-speed. It sort of confused the hitters and the umpires, too. It acted like a grease ball, but wasn't. I also toyed with a screwball. And although everyone was convinced by then that I was throwing a grease ball, I found I didn't need to do anything to the baseball. Simple natural oils from my fingertips and sweat seemed to give me all the moisture I needed. But I definitely intended to perpetuate the belief that I was throwing the illegal greaser.

Let me show you why. In August, 1970, I was leading the Reds, 3–2, in the top of the eighth. They had a man on second, two out, Pete Rose at bat. He was looking for one pitch.

"Okay, Perry," Pete shouted. "Let's see it. Let's see it."

He fouled off a fast ball, then worked me to a 3–1 count. Now he's positive he's going to get my alleged money pitch. So I came in with a changeup. He watched it float by for a strike. He looked at me funny and coiled himself up again. And I served up another changeup that seemed like the world had suddenly slipped into slow-motion. Pete just watched it and watched it and watched it, unable to gear up his swing as it drifted through the heart of the plate. He stood there for a few moments, looked at the plate, then at me and then walked slowly back to the dugout. He turned only to say, "Perry, you make me sick."

Later Rose said, "What can I say? That was the best pitch Perry's ever thrown me. Man, it just didn't figure."

That 1970 season was fine for me, but a disaster for

the Giants. After five straight second-place finishes for the Giants, Clyde King decided we'd think our way to the pennant. In spring training, he hired an expert in psycho-cybernetics to help us out.

"What is this psycho-what-ever-it-is all about?" Willie Mays asked Jimmy Davenport.

"Concentration," said Davenport. "He wants you to concentrate."

"Concentrate? What's he think I've been doing for the past 20 years?"

"Maybe," said Davenport, "if you'd learned this concentration bit a few years ago, Willie, you'd have 800 homers instead of those lousy 600 you've got."

The psycho-cybernetics lasted four sessions. Our next mistake was nine exhibition games in Japan. On our flight there, the captain announced that the temperature in Tokyo was 33 degrees. Japanese women fans met our plane with masks over their mouths because of the cold air. It warmed up the next day. It was 40 degrees for our first workout. Tokyo Stadium, we soon discovered, was Candlestick Far East. It had a wind, only colder, that blew straight in from center field. To keep us warm, there was a bucket of burning charcoal between two batting cages. There was one shower and a big tub to bathe in. Just like Farm Life, North Carolina.

Most everybody came down with a cold. We lost six of nine games in Japan, but the trip wasn't a total loss: I got to introduce my super-sinker to Shimonoseki, a seaport city on the tip of the island of Kyushu.

Warming up, I gave it the full treatment, every decoy I had, and the fans, who had heard about me, went wild. The Japanese cheerleaders on the dugout roofs began mimicking my motions. They went to their heads, necks, ears, backs of neck and screamed and cheered. This went on until the plate umpire, Kasuo Kuboyama, called over an interpreter and came out to the mound.

"No. No. No can do that in Japan," I was told.

185

"Do what? Do what?" I asked.

"No do that in Japan."

"I'm not doing anything."

"No do that," the umpire pointed his fingers toward me and then dipped them down sharply. Pelekoudas couldn't have been any clearer.

But the thing that really broke us up was when the ex-premier of Japan, Nobuske Kish, threw out the first pitch in the opening game ceremony. He wet his fingers on his lips before throwing the ball. He explained to me that he could never throw a baseball, even as a boy, without wetting his fingers. And I told him, "Well, sir, neither could I."

We broke our string of second-place finishes in 1970. We finished third. Clyde King lost the managing job early in the season, and Charlie Fox got hired.

After the season, my brother Jim and I were honored in a banquet of barbecue and Brunswick stew at the Williamston High School gym. There was a big parade planned before the banquet, but a heavy rain forced it to be cancelled. Dick Dietz was the guest speaker that rainy night. "I should have known anything connected with Gaylord would be wet and slippery," he said.

18

The conversation was depressing.

"I tell you, he'll hit his six hundredth against us," said young Bobby Bonds.

"Well, it isn't automatic, you know," Chris Speier insisted.

"If anybody's automatic, it's Hank," said Don McMahon.

"I wonder who the lucky guy will be?" said Dick Dietz.

We were sitting in a coffee shop in Atlanta, the afternoon of April 27, 1971, discussing the inevitable. Henry Aaron had hit his 599th home run the previous day.

"Aaron has a thing going against us," said Ron Bryant. "He hit number 500 off Mike McCormick and number 550 off me."

I finally spoke up. "I'm not enjoying this," I said. "I'm pitching tonight."

An Atlanta reporter wrote that afternoon, "Perry is one of the hardest pitchers for Hammering Hank to homer on. The last time [and only time] Aaron homered off Perry was July 16, 1964, almost seven years ago. Aaron has 17 home runs off Don Drysdale, his number one victim. Hank has hit Sandy Koufax with seven and Juan Marichal with six."

I had no desire to get my name in any record book—even Aaron's personal record book. If he was going to get No. 600 off me, he was going to earn it.

He did. He hit a high inside fast ball out of the park in the third inning.

"I was guessing fast ball," Aaron said. "I wanted to hit it quick because I was afraid I might see his curve or that crazy pitch later in the game."

The only other living man who had hit 600 home runs —Willie Mays—took some of the pleasure out of Aaron's night. We won, 6–5, in ten innings; Willie knocked in the winning run.

Mays was always fascinated by Babe Ruth's 714 home runs. I'll always remember him saying, "714? How can anybody hit that many? I hit 600 and I know how hard it is."

But that April night in 1971 he admitted, "Hank just might catch Ruth."

At the end of the 1971 season, Charlie Fox traded me to Cleveland for Sam McDowell. The one consolation was, I'd never give Henry No. 714.

I must admit I enjoyed my duels with Aaron. In nine seasons, he went 31 for 101 against me, for a .307 average, with 13 runs batted in. But I don't miss pitching to him, and I don't suppose he misses me. I'll never forget when he flipped me a couple of baseballs before a game. On each, he had scribbled an "X" mark, and a message. It said: "Spit here, Gay."

A lot of people have asked me what's the best way to pitch against Aaron. I always said, "Very carefully." Hank was forever stepping out of the batter's box when I was about to deliver the ball. He told writers he thought the delaying tactics would help dry out the ball.

For me, 1971 was a frustrating season. I didn't especially like Charlie Fox's five-man rotation, even though it gave me an extra day of rest, and I didn't find Fox was a big fan of mine. I had a better spring training, but Fox named Marichal to open the season.

It was a fairly uneventful season for shakedowns by the umpires, partly because I was going more and more to a fork ball and screwball and partly because I went a month and a half in the middle of the season without a victory. When I hit a dry spell like that, the umpires assumed I'd gone dry. They stopped searching me. And that I didn't like. I mean, I didn't spend all those seasons building up a reputation for it to be ruined in one year. Umpire Sudol saved the day for me in mid-July when he came out and took off my cap. The pictures made the wire services, and I told the writers, "I'm never happy about showing my head, but I was kind of glad to see Ed. I haven't seen an umpire in five weeks."

I did undergo one of my all-time favorite searches in Cincinnati that year. Four umpires surrounded me before I even got to the foul line in the first inning. I said, "Hey, what are you guys doing? Ain't you gonna let me pitch?"

Reds' manager Sparky Anderson had demanded that I get a full field inspection. By then I had pretty much stopped slickering the ball, but I liked to have something around just in case I got into a jam. That day, it was beneath the "V" in my uniform shirt at the neck. The umpires searched my cap, belt, neck, ears and certain areas I don't have to mention. But they missed the good spot.

"He's cleaner than a bone," Augie Donatelli yelled to Anderson, who smiled and waved a thank-you.

Well, I thought to myself, *for old time's sake, I'm gonna have some fun.* I retired Rose and Lee May in the first inning and then Tony Perez came to the plate. I got my fingers slicky while the ball was being thrown around the infield and I threw Perez an outstanding super drop. He missed it by a foot. Sparky was up on the top step screaming. I mixed in a fork ball which moved like a greaser, and Perez fouled it into the dirt. They were all yelling in the Cincy dugout. And then, maybe I shouldn't have, but I threw another super drop and Perez missed it by a mile.

Anderson came running out of the dugout screaming and pointing. Donatelli took off his mask and said, "Sparky, shut up. We searched him and he has nothing. He's not throwing anything illegal. Now if you don't sit down and be quiet, I'm gonna clean the bench. I don't want to hear another word about that pitch."

Well, you can guess what I did the rest of that night. Sparky was near apoplexy. He couldn't even complain. But it served him right for having me so thoroughly checked before I even got to the mound.

We won our division title, and I won the first game of the play-offs, 5–4, over the Pirates. Then I blew the deciding game to the Pirates, who went on to win that Series.

The pressure was really on my super drop during the playoffs. It was my first post-season play, and all the network TV people were trying to find out about it. One of those sportscasters came over to where my daughter Allison, then five years old, was sitting. Microphone in hand, he asked, "What's your name, honey?"

"Allison Perry."

"Are you here rooting for your daddy?"

"Unhuh. Yes, sir."

"Your daddy's quite a pitcher, isn't he?"

"Mommy says so."

"Your daddy has quite a reputation for throwing a funny pitch. They say he uses grease. But nobody knows where he keeps it. Do you, Allison?"

"Unhuh. At home in the garage."

"Well, isn't that cute? Does your daddy throw a grease ball, honey?"

Can you imagine the nerve, asking that question?

"It's a hard slider," said Allison. Interview ended.

I finished 16–12 with a 2.76 ERA, and shortly after the Giants told me I wouldn't be traded, Tom Haller called to tell me I had been traded to the Cleveland Indians. Charlie Fox had been trying to get the Giants to sign Sam McDowell ever since Sam was in high school.

I ran into Ray Fosse, the Cleveland catcher and player representative, at the players' meetings in Acapulco right after the trade was announced.

"Can you catch it?" I kidded him.

"Gaylord," he said. "I'd love to try. I'm looking forward to spring training right now."

I flew home as quick as I could because Blanche likes to say what she thinks to the papers and I wasn't sure what she thought about it all. The kids showed their feelings by going to school the next day with their San Francisco Giants T-shirts turned inside out.

I asked them, "What you doing that for?"

"Because we ain't Giants no more."

Indians' manager Kenny Aspromonte called and we talked briefly. "All I want is the chance to pitch every fourth day," I said.

Kenny chuckled. "With our club?" he said. "How 'bout every third day?"

The reason for the trade was the Giants' desperate need for a left-handed pitcher. And they figured they were gaining four years in age in the younger McDowell. I had won more games the previous four seasons, but he

191

had been playing for a club that couldn't play .500 ball and the Giants reasoned that Sam would win 20 games easily for them.

I only knew Sam by reputation. He can really give the boys some quotes. He told the San Francisco press, "I think the Giants gave up too much to get me. But I've known Charlie for a long time and he's a fantastic man. If he'd ask me to walk through a stone wall, I'd give it a helluva try."

I was gratified by Gabe Paul's remark when the deal was made. The Cleveland general manager said, "Gaylord has a young body. He keeps in shape. I'll bet Gaylord is still pitching after Sam has quit."

They had a banquet for me in San Francisco before I left for spring training. McDowell came and offered one of his philosophies of pitching. Sam said, "Almost every batter guesses at least a few times every game. This is an advantage for me. Trying to think with me is a mismatch. I'm too unpredictable. Hell, most of the time I don't know where the pitch is going to wind up, or even what I'm going to throw to begin with."

My old friend Chris Pelekoudas showed up, too. He announced that he wished to give me a going-away present. I stripped away the gift wrapping, opened a box and found a one-pound jar of vaseline. I needed two hands to hold it up to the crowd.

There was even a card: "From your friend, Chris. Good luck."

Pelekoudas stood up and said, "That should last you through the season."

I replied, "But what am I going to do for August and September?"

I was kidding, of course.

19

· · · · · ·

August 19, 1972

Mr. Joseph E. Cronin
American League
520 Boylston Street
Boston, Massachusetts 02116

Dear Joe:

The harassment of Gaylord Perry has reached such proportions that I feel obliged to enter a protest over the procedures in force since the directive from your office permitting managers to request a "shakedown" of Perry at their own discretion. . . .

Last night there was a disgraceful exhibition by Mike Epstein after he struck out in the fourth inning. He was screaming all over the place, ran one-third of the way to the mound with a bat in his hand and then, when he was fully restrained, Dick Williams, using every tactic at his disposal, requested the umpires to examine Perry. The entire affair took eight minutes and when play resumed Sal Bando hit the first pitch for a home run. . . .

It is very obvious that the directive from your office permitting the managers to pick the time and place for harassment is having its effect on our club. This should not be permitted.

Are these players within their rights to carry bats toward the mound, threaten, curse and demonstrate and escape without penalty while their club uses this as a means of upsetting the pitcher who has no protection whatsoever? We are requesting that the directive authorizing the managers of opposing clubs to call their shots and inspect Perry whenever they wish be immediately rescinded and that steps be taken to protect players of any team who are being threatened by players of the opposing club.

Please allow Perry to do his work without this unnecessary and unfair harassment which very definitely gives the opposing team a new advantage which they are using cleverly. . . .

> *Very truly yours,*
> CLEVELAND INDIANS, INC.
> *Gabriel Paul*
> *General Manager*

I thought I'd had a tough time in the National League: Pelekoudas watching over me like a vulture, Mauch screaming from the third-base coaching box, Durocher using words that would embarras a longshoreman, Henry Aaron grumbling at me from April to October. But all of that was nothing compared to the excitement I created in the American League: an official protest of a game by a manager, an official protest of harassment

194

against me by the Indians, Mike Epstein and Tony Oliva threatening me with their bats, a national TV show on me and my grease ball.

And because of my phantom pitch, two players were fined $600, two managers were thumbed out of games, one being suspended and fired by his team. It's a wonder I was able to squeeze in any pitching.

The first time I faced Oakland, we had some real excitement. In the fourth inning, the game scoreless, Mike Epstein came to bat. He was grumbling 'cause I'd struck him out in the first inning. He was bending plate ump Hank Morgenweck's ear, and it didn't take a genius to guess the topic. Once they're thinking about a slicky pitch, I'm in command. I'd usually go to my rising fast ball or hard slider. When the hitter is looking for the ball at his knee caps he can't get around on the stuff upstairs. Epstein clearly was too upset to hit anything. I know it sounds cruel, but I served nothing but my sinkers and fork balls, stuff that looked like greasers. He couldn't swing a bat, he got so mad.

"You cheatin' SOB, play this game like a man," he screamed.

"Get back in the box," Morgenweck snapped. "Play ball."

I shot another little dipper to Epstein and he missed it by a foot. He shook his bat at me and started for the mound, screaming threats.

"Throw me another spitter and I'm coming for you."

I turned my back on Epstein. If he wanted me so bad, he could have come right to the mound. Talk is cheap. Epstein reminded me of a young bull in the pasture back home. When he'd get mad, he'd snort and paw the ground in a mean way. But any bull that does that is just bluffing. The next day, I heard Epstein's manager, Dick Williams, had delighted in the whole thing. "I wish Epstein would have gone to the mound," Williams supposedly said. "Gaylord would have killed him." There was no love lost between them; during the 1972 World Series, they had a shouting match on the team plane between Cincinnati and Oakland. Mike was traded that winter for a bag of marbles.

Epstein's bat-waving threat—followed by Dick Williams' search-on-demand triggered Gabe Paul's letter to Joe Cronin. Paul said, "This is a damned joke. The idea that a manager at any time can decide he wants Perry dressed down is a crock. Epstein was provoking a riot. He should have been thrown out of the game. Doesn't Gaylord have any rights? He's never been found guilty of a thing."

I sure did appreciate Gabe Paul's verbal and moral support, and I sure wish he would've felt the same way the next year when he was with the Yankees and Ralph Houk, the Yankee manager, wanted me stripped from head to toe. But by then, Gabe Paul—like Chub Feeney before him—had gone over to the so-called dry side of the fence. But, that's life.

I lost to Oakland, 3–2, in ten innings, and the next day, with young Vince Colbert on the mound for us, Reggie Jackson halted play. He stood on home plate, turned, pointed at me in the dugout and demanded the umpires check the baseball. One of Colbert's pitches had just sunk an unreal amount. Reggie thought I might be sharing my evil secrets. Other people got the same suspicion; they began calling the Indian pitching staff "The Great Slime."

The next Epstein-Perry confrontation came at the end of August in Oakland. Epstein was calm—for him—but in the sixth inning, Dick Williams came charging out of the dugout. "I think he's got it on his shirt," snapped Williams. "We want him checked."

"Okay, Dick," said Jim Evans, the plate umpire. Nester Chylak, the crew chief, looked into the fingers of my glove, felt my belt, then looked at Williams.

"Damn it, I'm no chemist, I don't know if anything's

on his shirt," Chylak shouted. "Gaylord, I'm going to ask you to change shirts. I don't know if anything's on it or not. But change the shirt, and we'll take care of Mr. Williams."

"Of course," I said. "Glad to."

I had to fight hard to keep from smiling. Before coming out for that inning, I had taken off my shirt that was full of sweat and grease (from baby oil and capsolin). If they wanted me to change again, I didn't mind. I took off the clean shirt and put back on the slicky one. It was a perfect maneuver: Williams was satisfied, the umpires were satisfied, and of course I was satisfied. I overheard Chylak say to Williams, "We've checked him and he's clean. He's changed shirts. That's it, Dick. That's your last complaint of the ball game. Unless we see Perry doing something wrong, we're not going out there again."

Williams' strategy may have backfired for a moment, but I've got to admit one thing: the two years I pitched for Cleveland and he managed Oakland, I never did beat the A's, not once.

Chuck Tanner of the White Sox was one of my first adversaries in the American League. In a game where I beat the White Sox, 2–1, Tanner informed umpire Bill Haller he was protesting the game because I was throwing "an illegal pitch."

"If we don't win the protest, Perry will be free to use his grease ball all the time," said Tanner. "There'll be a rush on the market for the jelly he uses."

Haller said he couldn't see that I was doing anything illegal, and then Cronin threw out the formal protest. Tanner said, "There is nothing left now but to teach the same pitch to our kids." I replied, "I'm not doing anything illegal. I'll be interested to see what Chuck's gonna teach 'em."

The next time I faced the White Sox, I found out how Tanner was going to counterattack. He waited until a crucial point in the game with his big hitter up. Then out he came. The score was 1–0, my favor, and Dick Allen was the batter. Tanner called time and had umpire Merle Anthony frisk me. Four pitches later, Allen hit a home run to tie the game and I lost it in the ninth. Tanner's tactic inspired Williams', and Williams', in turn, inspired Gabe Paul's protest.

Cronin ruled in favor of Gabe. "I've told Dick Butler [supervisor of American League umpires] to instruct the umpires to use their own good judgment when the situation arises," Cronin said. "They are not obliged to check Perry every time somebody asks them to. If, in their opinion, Perry is not suspect, they have every right to say 'no' to opposing managers."

Cronin later praised umpire Bill Kunkel, who worked the plate in my nineteenth victory, 3–2, over the Twins in Cleveland. "Kunkel handled it just as I want all the umpires to handle it in the future," said Cronin. "He inspected Perry once, but wouldn't allow [Minnesota manager] Frank Quilici on the field at the time. After Kunkel was satisfied that Perry was doing nothing wrong, that was it. That's the way it should be."

Well, there's a lot more to Kunkel's shakedown than that. A few days earlier, a Cleveland store called Gaylord's Discount Department Store had filmed a skit to run as a commercial on television. In the skit, I played a pitcher, Ray Fosse played my catcher and Kunkel was hired to portray an umpire. Here's how it went:

UMPIRE: *Sorry, Gaylord, let's take a look.* (He checks Gaylord for grease.)
GAYLORD: *What are you doing tonight, Ray?*
FOSSE: *Oh my wife wants me to go shopping with her and the kids for some clothes 'n' things.* (Umpire continues to check Gaylord for grease. Fosse starts to leave.)

198

UMPIRE:	*Where ya going, Ray?*
FOSSE:	*To Gaylord's.*
GAYLORD:	*My house? I thought you were going shopping.*
FOSSE:	*I am—to Gaylord's.*
UMPIRE:	*Which is it? Gaylord's or shopping?*
FOSSE:	*We're going to* Gaylord's.
GAYLORD:	*My house for shopping?*
FOSSE:	*No. . . I mean yes. . . Gaylord's—Gaylord's Discount Department Store.*
UMPIRE & GAYLORD:	*Why didn't you say so?*
VOICE:	*Go Gaylord's, where you always wind up a winner.*

The night after we shot that commercial, I pitched against the Twins and Kunkel worked behind the plate. I had good stuff that night, and the Twins started putting up a fuss. Even Harmon Killebrew said, "Darn it." So Quilici demanded an inspection.

Kunkel told Quilici, "There is nothing on Gaylord. I haven't seen one suspicious pitch. He's got a good sinker and hard slider."

"I don't care. My boys are screaming. I want Perry checked over."

"Okay, you stay here. I'll give him the once-over."

Out came Kunkel with Fosse next to him, and Kunkel said, "Sorry, Gaylord, let's take a look."

"What are you doing tonight, Ray?" I asked Fosse, just like in the script. And Ray picked up the rest of it. Poor Kunkel. He couldn't laugh out loud, and for his sake, neither could we. I want to say that Kunkel did his job. He did search me. So there was no harm in having a little fun.

One of the good things about coming to Cleveland was that my off-the-field income went up to about $20,000 a year. I never made any kind of money off the field in San Francisco. I was way down the totem pole for commercials and endorsements. We had guys like Marichal, Mays, McCovey and Cepeda who got all the big ones.

I had some close calls, though. Once a city slicker from Madison Avenue approached me about a commercial since I was accused of using greasy kid stuff hair tonic. He phoned me up in New York and asked if we could get together on it. I told him to meet me at the ball park. I was on the field when he arrived. He was very enthusiastic until I took off my cap. When he saw my bald head, he turned green.

"Well, what do I say now?" he stammered.

"Goodbye," I suggested.

My brother Jim and I finally latched on to a razor commercial, and once I modeled a sweater in a magazine. For payment, I got a dozen sweaters, all the same style and color. At least they were all the same size, too.

With all the talk about Vaseline and my so-called grease ball, an agent friend of mine, Frank Hadfield, phoned the Vaseline people to see if they'd like me to give the product some kind of endorsement.

He got one of the vice presidents of the company. He turned us down with a terrific line: "We soothe babies' asses, not baseballs," he said.

I was sky-high for the 1972 season with Cleveland. I have nothing but respect for the Giants but I wanted to have an outstanding year, mostly as a matter of personal pride.

In spring training, the American League umpires hobnobbed with Pelekoudas and the other National League umps and asked about me and my dipsy-doodle. Of course, all my old Giant teammates were in Arizona, too.

The first time we went to Phoenix to play the Giants, I made it a point to look up Pelekoudas. I knocked on the door to the umpires' quarters. Chris said, "Come in."

"Chris, how you been? Good to see you," I smiled.

"Gaylord, how are you? It's good to see you again. Especially in an American League uniform."

"I just came over to wish you good luck," I said. "I'm gonna miss you."

"Gaylord, good luck yourself. Put her there." He smiled and held out his hand. I grabbed his hand, and he gave out a little scream.

"You son of a gun, you got me," said Pelekoudas. He laughed and looked down at his hand smeared thick with Vaseline. Pelekoudas turned to the American League umpires he was working with and said, "See what you boys are going to have to put up with this year?"

I started against my ex-teammates, with Pelekoudas umpiring at third base. I think John Rice was behind the plate. Bobby Bonds came up, and I looked at Pelekoudas, and he grinned. What the heck, I thought, for old time's sake. Standing there, I felt a little trickle of sweat roll into my palm and accidentally my fingers went to it as if a reflex action. I let Fosse know a "sinker" was coming. The pitch came in and died at the plate, and Bonds missed it by a foot. Bobby paused and doffed his cap to me. The crowd at Hi-Corbett field laughed and applauded. But they didn't know what was going on. Bonds did. So did Pelekoudas, who broke into a grin. As we trotted off the field, Fosse had a look of pure pleasure on his face. He had caught that dipsy-doodle like it was nothing. It may have been the first one he ever saw. He seemed relaxed for the first time that spring.

I didn't put anything on that pitch to Bonds but sweat. I had discovered the season before that if I didn't dry my fingers, there was always some natural moisture on the tips. By the time I got to Cleveland, I really did have a sweat ball that no one could outlaw except the good Lord. I developed an excellent fork ball, too, hard fork ball. It's tough to get people to believe I actually throw a fork ball. Even some of my own teammates are skeptical.

There is no way I could have won 24 games that

season without Fosse. The first thing my brother, Jim, told me when he heard about the trade was that I'd be pitching to the best catcher in the league. Fosse can throw, he has quickness behind the plate and good hands. But more important, Fosse knew the American League batters. The Indians' pitching staff was young and inexperienced. Manager Ken Aspromonte had just spent five years coaching and managing in the minors and pitching coach Warren Spahn had been doing the same.

The first American League manager to get on me was Billy Martin, who was in Detroit, but knew my brother from Minnesota. "I'm waiting to see that wet garbage, I'm waiting to see the cheating brother put on his act," Billy said the first time we met. It was mid-May, and I was already going for my seventh victory. Martin was all over plate umpire Lou DiMuro, until DiMuro finally came to the mound to look at the hair on the *back* of my head.

"Martin wants me to feel your hair," DiMuro apologized.

"Be my guest. Do I have to take off my cap?"

"Sorry," he said, removing my lid. There was a gasp and then a roar of laughter from the Tiger fans.

I won the game. I retired 15 Tigers in a row. DiMuro found nothing.

Later in the year, in Cleveland, Martin brought a bloodhound to the ball park. He had the dog sniffing Vaseline and stuff on baseballs. The dog was supposed to run out of the stands to sniff me. I heard about the dog, but I never did see him. I guess he never learned to sniff right. I heard that Billy said, "Cronin won't believe me, but he might believe my dog."

I pitched in the All-Star game, my third, in Atlanta, and I made the hometown fans happy by giving up a home run to Henry Aaron, his second in All-Star competition. The one consolation was that it didn't count toward 714.

Aaron said afterward his homer came off "a spitball,

down and in." I'd like to set the record straight: if it had been a spitter, he wouldn't have hit it.

By the first of August, I had 18 victories and a 1.63 ERA. I lost six of my next eight games, but on September 9, I became the first pitcher in half a century to become a 20-game winner in both major leagues.

I finished up 24–16 and eight of those 16 losses were by one run. I had 40 appearances and 342⅔ innings, the most for an Indian since Bob Lemon hurled 387 in 1953. I struck out 234 and walked 82 with a 1.92 earned run average. Not bad for a thirty-four-year-old pitcher. The Indians added a year on my two-year contract at $100,000. And just to make everything perfect, I won the Cy Young Award as the best pitcher in the American League.

One sportswriter left me off his Cy Young ballot entirely. His explanation was that he couldn't vote for me because I threw an illegal pitch. Some people just refuse to believe that a man is innocent until proven guilty.

20

June 26, 1973

Mr. Joseph E. Cronin
American League
520 Boylston Street
Boston, Massachusetts 02116

Dear Joe:

The harassment of Gaylord Perry has reached such proportions that I feel obliged to enter a protest over the procedures in force since the directive from your office permitting managers to shakedown Perry at their own discretion.

Last night there was a disgraceful exhibition by Ralph Houk. He was screaming all over the place and *ran all the way to the mound when he was finally restrained. Houk, using every tactic at his disposal, requested the umpires to examine Perry. The entire affair took ten minutes.*

It is very obvious that the directive from your office permitting the managers to pick the time and place for harassment is having its effect on our club. This should not be permitted.

Please allow Perry to do his work without this unnecessary and unfair harassment which very definitely gives the opposing team a new advantage which they are using cleverly.

> *Very truly yours,*
> CLEVELAND INDIANS, INC.
> *Phil Seghi*
> *General Manager*

Seghi never mailed this parody of Gabe Paul's letter to Joe Cronin, but he was tempted to. It really was a funny situation. Gabe Paul had left the Indians to become vice-president of the Yankees, and, suddenly, I went from hero in his mind to villain.

The amazing transformation took place on the night of June 25 in Cleveland. I had a 4–2 lead over the Yankees in the top of the eighth. With Horace Clarke on third, Matty Alou hit a shot off my shinbone. I retrieved the ball in time to throw Clarke out at the plate—according to plate umpire Lou DiMuro, but not according to the Yankees. They argued for a while, and then the game resumed. My first pitch to Roy White was a sinker. Ralph Houk, the Yankee manager, charged out to the mound, yanked my cap off my head and started looking inside the lining.

"I'm gonna find where you keep it," he shouted. "I've had it. Let's see inside that cap."

"Ralph, what you doing?" I said. "I got nothing to hide."

205

DiMuro joined us on the run.

"You're getting it from somewhere and I'm gonna find it," Houk snapped. "Check everything, Lou. The wrist. The belt. How 'bout back of the belt? The glove? No? The neck, that's the place. Not there either? Then the hair and the forehead. . . ."

DiMuro looked everywhere, and Houk's nose was right with him.

"This is ridiculous," Houk bellowed. "We all know he's putting something on the ball."

"You know you're not supposed to be out here," DiMuro warned.

"I know. I couldn't help it. I just couldn't take any more sitting down." Houk held my cap to his nose.

"Hey, I smell something in his cap. Smell this cap, Lou."

"The Indians only give us one a season," I warned.

"It stinks," Houk said.

"I'm not smelling nobody's cap," said DiMuro. "You're making a circus out of this. Ralph, he's clean. Now get off the field."

I sure don't know what Ralph was looking for, but if I'd had anything, I'd have gotten rid of it before he crossed the third-base line. He's a strong fellow.

Things kinda calmed down for about 33 seconds. Then White chopped my next pitch foul just outside the third-base line. Third-base coach Dick Howser raced in and scooped up the ball before Buddy Bell, our third baseman could retrieve it. Howser began screaming. "Look at this. It's got a grease spot." He was pointing to a spot on the ball. "Here's the stuff right here."

DiMuro blew his cork because Howser had no business picking up the ball along the foul line. "All I see is dirt," said DiMuro. Howser used a few special words: "Perry's throwing it pitch after pitch and you do nothing. You guys are a joke." DiMuro threw Howser out of the game.

I won the game, and later, in the visiting clubhouse, Bobby Murcer held court with the writers. He said, "Perry throws it 99 percent of the time. If they ever ban that pitch, he'll be out of baseball. It's a jelly substance. You can't see it, but it's slippery. The umpires' hands are tied. They don't get any help. If the league president or commissioner had any guts, they'd ban the pitch—and you can print that. I want them to see it."

The commissioner saw it and called Murcer to his office and fined him $250 for his "gutless" remark. But Murcer still didn't back off. "The commissioner told me I should be more discreet in my comments. . . but Perry throws the grease ball."

My reaction? I told the writers, "I'm back on the beam again. I haven't had so much fun since last season. When they came out to check me, I finally felt at home. I don't remember anyone in my whole career getting as mad as Houk did."

I don't know why Murcer was so upset. He batted .571 against me in 1973. I guess he wasn't really angry. He sent me a gallon jar of expensive cooking oil with a note: "Dear Gaylord, here's a jar of the best. I know you want to go first class."

Then my former boss, Gabe Paul, announced that the Yankees would have closed-circuit television on me for the purpose of "catching me in the act" when I got to Yankee Stadium. And Gabe had protested that I was being harassed the year before. It didn't bother me. "They can take all the pictures they want," I said. "Just tell Gabe to save me a copy of the film, will you?"

Gabe withdrew his plan when it was announced that ABC-TV was going to film me, and Howard Cosell and Bobby Bragan were going to provide some expert analysis. My old friend Bragan had become president of the Texas League and a member of baseball's rules committee. I figured to have some fun so I came up with another decoy, just for Howard and Bobby, and they fell for it hook, line and sinker. I added a wipe under my armpit just for them. Unfortunately, the Yankees wiped me out, 7–2. Then Bragan wiped me out with the neatest decoy I've ever seen.

Bragan came into the clubhouse after the game and I was still upset about my defeat. He was telling reporters, "Truthfully, I can't tell if Gaylord is doctoring the ball. I can't see where he is getting anything. All I could do was guess. There were a few questionable pitches."

Then Bobby and I joined Cosell, and all of a sudden, Bragan had all the evidence he needed to call me a "spitballer." Here's what he said on camera: "I got to believe he does [throw an illegal pitch] and he's in select company. He's not the only one. It's not like indicting John Dillinger or Al Capone. There are a lot of other criminals roaming the woods."

After viewing playbacks of me on the mound, Bragan said, "The ball goes downward. There's no question about it being doctored. It looks like. . . he's going to the armpit. That might be where he's getting that greasy kid stuff. That K-Y jelly."

"Ha, ha, ha," Cosell laughed.

"There he goes again to the armpit . . ."

"Ha, ha, ha," Cosell laughed.

My good friend Bragan certainly decoyed me. He showed me two faces. But anything for show business, right? I don't mind the publicity for being suspected of throwing the pitch. But I was taken under false pretenses into that situation. Besides, maybe Brash Bobby Bragan doesn't realize that the spitter went out six years before. He misnamed the popular illegal pitch. It's the greaser the boys are throwing now. And Brash Bobby fell for my armpit decoy. If I were grease balling, would I put my supply in such an obvious place and then reach across to load up? C'mon.

Seghi filed a protest with the commissioner's office in New York about the bizarre television investigation.

Seghi described it as a "telescopic witchhunt " and "Kangaroo court." "They put Perry on trial and convicted him without proof and I want to see some kind of retraction," Seghi said. Aspromonte said I should sue. I'll say one thing, they do things up big in New York.

As for that ball game, when Murcer came to bat in the first inning I unloaded all the decoys I could think of, including taking off my cap and wiping the sweat off the top of my bald head. The fans booed. Bobby grounded out. But the next time I blew the whole thing with a hanging slider that Murcer hit for a two-run homer. Roy White hit another pair of dingers and I was an ignominious loser, 7–2.

After the game, Murcer phoned up our clubhouse and asked me to meet his wife. I thought that was very nice. Bobby introduced her to me and when I reached out to shake her hand I knew I had been had. She had some kind of smelly perfumed cream spread all over her hand.

Bobby's parting shot to me was, "I guess we gave you another chapter for your book, huh?"

It was a session full of agitation for players and managers. Whitey Herzog replaced Ted Williams as manager of the Rangers, not the best job in the world. While Whitey is about half Williams' size he's got vocal pipes to match Ted's. He never let up on that first trip into Arlington, Texas in May.

In the seventh inning with us ahead 2–1 (we're always ahead when this sort of thing erupts) Herzog loaded one up in the dugout. Then he came galloping out of the dugout waving the ball. He claimed that the Ranger ball boy, Steve Macko, had retrieved a greased-up ball fouled onto the screen. Herzog was cursing and stamping up and down on his cap. And he got himself thrown out of the game by plate umpire Art Frantz. They tell me he showed Frantz a ball with enough grease on it to lubricate a Sherman tank.

Honochick said, "Herzog's a joke. Coming out of the

dugout with a ball like that. He never even asked us to check Perry. He was just trying to wake up his club." He did. They came back and beat me, 3–2. But that was the last I heard from Whitey. He got tired of complaining, then he got fired the last week of the season. The Rangers mailed Herzog's ball to Cronin's office. It was deemed inadmissible evidence. The league ran a chemical analysis of baseballs I had thrown last year and reported me clean.

Mike Epstein was traded from the A's to the Rangers to the Angels, since the previous season. He said nothing about me being a cheater. When the Californians came in for a visit he hit a two-run homer off me. "What's the use," he told the writers. "Sure, Perry still throws 'em. But I can't complain any more because everybody in the league, it seems, is throwing the same thing now. I'm not going to get caught up in the controversy any more." It couldn't be that the Angels have a fine stable of pitchers accused of throwing my phantom pitch: like Bill Singer, Clyde Wright and Dave Sells.

Cepeda let me have it pretty good last summer. In the ninth inning, I had an 8–2 lead over Boston and got him on a soft fly ball. When he passed me on the mound he said, "You got a five-run lead and you still throw me spitters? You cheating s.o.b." Then he got to the dugout and screamed, "You bald-headed (beep beep). You no good (beep beep). Throw that wet junk. It's all you got." I had been in the worst slump of my career and nobody had paid much attention to me for three weeks. I had won only two of my previous eleven games when I got going again. Maybe it was Orlando's encouraging words.

Even gentle Del Crandall came unstuck in '73. Umpire John Flaherty came out to check my hair. He flicked it a little and Crandall said, "John, I don't think you're giving me your best effort. Maybe you don't have your heart in it." And Crandall turned and walked back to the Milwaukee bench. That game I fanned George Scott for my two-hundredth strike-out of the season. I called for the ball.

Crandall yelled, "What's that, your two hundredth greaser?" Now that just wasn't like Del.

About that time some guy came out with the "secret to Perry's grease ball." He said I used fly-line cleaner, a substance that fishermen rub on their fly line to keep it dry. When you touch it with water, it turns slick. I was said to work it into my fingers between innings, building a supply of it into the pores. My fingers, he said, were dry for the fast ball and slider, but when I wanted to load one up, I just rubbed my fingers against any part of my body that's sweating. I never heard of a fly-line cleaner but in the old days I'd have given it a try.

Singer made news at the All-Star game. Cincinnati manager Sparky Anderson said that a jacket worn by Singer showed up in the National League dressing room with a tube of lubricating jelly and a toothbrush in one of its pockets. Anderson said, "It might have been a joke, I'm not touching this thing with a ten-foot pole." Rose claimed Singer threw four straight spitballs in the game.

On Memorial Day we pulled into Chicago's Sheraton for a weekend series with the White Sox and Tanner was blowing hot already. The papers billed it as the meeting between me, "Mr. Moist," and Tanner, "Mr. Dry." Before I even put down my bags in the hotel the phone was ringing. The papers wanted a reply to Tanner's outburst. He had said, "If baseball is really serious about helping the hitters, then all it has to do is start having umpires call a ball for every pitch that they think is a spitter— whether the batter swings or not. One guy in the National League [Chris Pelekoudas] was doing this until the league stopped him."

Chuck was just psyching up for the weekend, protecting his boys. There's no way an umpire can guess what a pitch is. Tanner was trying to get the umpires set up against me, and I hadn't even pitched there that year.

The papers polled some of the Sox players to compare Singer, me and our phantom pitches. They gave me the slight edge. Dick Allen said, "I think Perry might have the better one." Catcher Ed Herrmann praised my control. I told the writers, "Glad to see they have me right up there. Guess I haven't lost whatever I'm supposed to have!"

There was a reason for all the 1973 agitation. Interleague trading had brought in some pitchers from the National League who were suspected of dipsy-doodles. The increase in the number of suspected illegal pitches caused some heat among players, managers and umpires.

It got to the kindling point between me and one umpire crew in Chicago one hot night in August. I had given up only five runs in my previous 27 innings and Tanner lost no time swinging into action. He demanded tiresome clothing checks in the first and second inning by plate ump Merl Anthony.

Bill Haller was at third base and the Sox bench was on him for my alleged grease ball. After the two inspections, Haller came at me pointing a finger and yelling, "I've had enough of this, enough." Then he said he would go to the commissioner's office. "We've taken enough abuse. We catch it from everybody. We're fed up."

That's the first time that happened. I told Haller, "Go ahead, I've got nothing to hide."

Tanner praised Haller to all the writers. "Bill stopped Perry from throwing the grease ball. I told the umpires, let's forfeit the game. Nobody can hit his pitches. I'd just as soon concede the game and come back fresh tomorrow. But Haller went out and talked to him. He had the guts to challenge Perry. Perry never threw another one. He beat us without it." That was baloney. I pitched the same the whole game, whichever way that was.

Tanner knew he couldn't bother me. But he sure could agitate umpires. I expect him to try it again this season. I don't blame him a bit. I respect him for his ingenuity. He always has something up his sleeve.

There is no other umpire like Pelekoudas, and you

can take that two ways. But Bill Haller is one of the three best umpires in the American League. One pitcher praised Haller, "He is the only umpire I know who pays attention when you're warming up and watches how your ball is running so he's prepared when the game begins."

Here's what Haller said in '73 about spitball charges: "I've never seen a spitter in the big leagues. I have seen them in the minors. But no umpire can see the rotation properly bent down calling balls and strikes. Managers come out and players complain. I really don't know what I'm supposed to be looking for."

Here's what he said about me: "I watched Gaylord like a hawk. He never goes to his mouth. I never see him get any foreign substance. When we umpire, we check the balls as well as the catcher's glove. I've never found anything. I'll tell you what he's got: a good curve, a fine fast ball, a good change and a fine sinker. His sinker is the suspicious one. It's excellent. But no better than Mel Stottlemyer's and they don't complain about his. I'll tell you what Perry is: he's one helluva pitcher, a fantastic competitor."

Like I say, Haller calls 'em like he sees 'em.

Earl Weaver of Baltimore really got on umpire Jim Odom during a game I won, 6–0, on a five-hitter. First-base coach George Staller claimed he found some "incriminating evidence" on the ball and took it to Weaver, who took it to plate umpire Odom. Odom didn't understand and Weaver threw up his hands and said, "Jim, did you ever see a spitter? Do you know what one looks like?"

"No," said Odom.

"You see? Dirt will stick in a brown spot where the grease is," said Weaver, who then ran the ball along the gravel on the warning track and showed him the spot that now had turned black.

"Still no? Okay, I'll have one of my guys tell you when Gaylord throws another one."

Tommy Davis was at bat, and on the second pitch,

Davis turned to Odom and said, "That was a spitball. It dropped a foot and a half." Catcher Johnny Ellis was cracking up, "Jeeze, everybody was talking all the time to Odom. I don't know why he didn't do anything."

My wife, Blanche, hates those shakedown inspections. So do the kids. "It's down right humiliating, that's what it is," Blanche says. "When I see those umpires go out there I skinch down as deep as I can in my seat. I don't look anymore. And all the fans around laugh and make all those remarks. At first, the kids would start to cry when they went out to get Gaylord. Our son Jack once had to be taken to the rest room, he was screaming so much. I guess we've gotten used to it some. But not really. Taking Gaylord's cap off is the worst. We're used to seeing his skin top but the fans were shocked everytime the cap came off.

"I don't get mad because I think Gaylord's asking for it. I guess he has to pull all those decoys. It's his career. At first I'd just hold my breath. That time in Oakland when they made him take off his pants, or something. When he was walking off the field, I didn't know if he was thrown out of the game, suspended or what. I hate to see the umpire wipe him with a towel. Ugh. But Gaylord doesn't get embarrassed. I just hate to see it break his rhythm. Of course, with all his decoys he's trying to do just that to the batter. Everybody asks me if he throws the grease ball. Lord, I don't know. All I know is what I read and hear and I just stay out of it. All I do is fix him the greasiest old steak I can find in the store. He takes over from there."

It was a big year for the Perry brothers. We finally met as opponents on the Fourth of July in Cleveland Stadium. My trade for McDowell made it possible and Jim was traded from Minnesota to Detroit during spring training. It was the first meeting of brothers in American League history. It had happened last in the National League four years earlier when Joe Niekro defeated his brother, Phil, 1–0.

Daddy called before the game and said, "I'm rooting for shutout pitching for both of you for nine innings and then let your relief pitchers take over to decide the winner." I told him, "No way I'm leaving a game with a shutout going."

Like I said, these big games in baseball are often floperoos. The Tigers won, 5–4. I took the loss but Jim didn't even get credit for the victory. Ed Farmer did in relief. Charlie Spikes had hit a disputed home run. Jim grumbled. "I should've won and I would've if the umpire hadn't called the ball wrong. There's no way that ball is fair, and you can ask anybody who was in our bullpen." Anyway, I left in the seventh inning and Jim in the sixth. Mamma and Daddy nearly got earaches trying to hear the game over the radio station in Cleveland. Daddy asked a reporter, "How'd they look? Boys been struggling this season. They ain't getting any younger. But that ain't it, I'm sure. I couldn't hear them because all the crackling doesn't die down on the radio until it gets dark about 8 o'clock."

At the end of the 1973 season, suddenly there were a lot of people talking a good grease ball game but not throwing one. I guess pitchers found out that it's better to be accused of throwing one, and say you don't, than telling everybody you do when you don't. Honesty is the best policy except when your fat wife asks you if you think she's fat, your boss asks you how you like his new suit, or when you break the rules in baseball. Cronin, both judge and jury, brought the hammer down on a couple of heads: first on Jim Merritt, who shut out Cleveland, 9–0, and said he did it with a spitball, and then on Billy Martin, who proudly told the sports world that he ordered two of his pitchers, Joe Coleman and Fred Sherman, to throw grease balls.

Merritt not only defeated me on the field that day but he defeated me in the clubhouse later, too, with his quotes. The Rangers' right-hander shut us out and then told anybody who would listen that he threw the illegal grease ball. "Yes I threw it," he said. "I'd say between 25 and 30. I may get in trouble for admitting it, but I did use the K-Y jelly that they say Gaylord uses." He was more accurate suggesting that he might get into trouble than he was about the effectiveness of his so-called greaser. Here I am accused of throwing one of the best in history and I'm denying it, and here he is throwing one nobody on our club noticed and proclaiming it to the world.

Merritt's greaser may have gone unnoticed by the hitters but his words were spotted by Cronin, who fined him $250. It was the best thing to happen to Merritt, a shutout and a fine by the league president. Merritt was seeking instant reputation. It was worth every penny of that $250 if he got batters thinking about a grease ball he may or may not throw. It's a boost to his career. Whether he has the greaser or not, if the batters believe he has it, he's going to be that much more effective.

It wasn't four days later that the grease ball accusations sent another career into a dive. During my 3–0 shutout of the Detroit Tigers, Billy Martin ordered his pitchers to throw spitballs the last two innings. After the game, Billy told the writers. "The umpires are making a mockery of the game by not stopping Perry. Everyone knows he does it and nobody does anything about it. We're going to keep on doing it every time he pitches against us. I did it to prove that it can be done without the umpires doing anything about it. For once in my life, I'd like to see baseball take a stand!"

It did. Cronin suspended Martin for three days, and before he got back Detroit general manager Jim Campbell fired him.

Coleman admitted putting Vaseline on the ball. "I had the Vaseline on my wrist and applied a little when I wanted it. I threw about 10 to 12 of them. . . and a couple were pretty good." Fred Sherman did not admit throwing an illegal pitch. He conceded that "if Billy said we did, OK."

Martin said, "If I'm fined I'll take it to a court of law. How can they fine you for telling the truth?" Billy didn't take it to a court of law. He took it to Arlington, Texas, where Rangers' owner Bob Short hired him seven days later to replace Whitey Herzog. My antagonists sure do get around.

As the season was nearing a close, I wasn't pitching like Cy Young. But I sure felt like him. I was 15–19 in September and needed four wins in a row to salvage the season. I believe in incentive, especially over the final weeks of a season when most players have become weary. Last year, for each of those final games I made a standing offer to teammates of $25 for each home run and $25 for two runs batted in and a ten-dollar steak dinner for three doubleplays. In my final four victories, the team had four homers and ten doubleplays. But I had to win the game before anybody could collect. If I lost, they got the Buynak Special (clubhouse man Cy Buynak's post-game snack).

I guess I've shelled out a couple of grand in bonuses since I started my incentive plans in 1966. At first I did it only for runs batted in and homers. But Maxie Lanier said one day, "Hey, how about something for my glove. I'm not one of those big hitters but I can help you win."

The main thing is I won my last four games to even my season's record at 19–19. I decided not to try for 20 against Baltimore with only two days' rest. It disappointed Oriole manager Weaver, however. He had set up television cameras, but not to try to catch me cheating. "Maybe we can find out how he does it, then maybe we'll try to copy him. We got some guys in our farm system who could use another pitch."

That last one was my toughest season since the early years of my career. If I threw the unhittable greaser, as

217

everyone complained, I sure was being cheated. My chance at having another fine year suffered a jolt in spring training when Ray Fosse was traded to Oakland for Dave Duncan, a catcher, and George Hendrick, an outfielder. It was a good trade for the club, two positions for one. But it was a severe setback for me, coming when it did at the end of spring training. Duncan had been a holdout with the A's and hardly played that spring, and we had no time to get to know each other before the season began. Then Duncan suffered a sore arm and then a broken wrist, and John Ellis and I had to get to know each other.

The hitters changed on me last year. They were swinging down and going the opposite way with the ball and getting base hits. I had to make an adjustment. I began to throw hard sliders up high. It was dangerous to throw up there and I got hurt but it would have been worse to stay down in the basement. The new designated hitter rule meant one more tough batter to face in the lineup, but all us pitchers had to live with that one.

I won the season opener, 2–1, over Detroit before 74,420—the largest crowd in my career—and I won the season finale, 1–0, against Boston before 1,453 fans. I struck out seven of the last ten batters I faced. For two seasons I had won 43 games for last-place Cleveland. The figure I'm most proud of is having pitched 325 or more innings for four of the previous five seasons. I've averaged 19 victories the last eight seasons and a career earned run average of 2.87. End of commercial.

Nobody really noticed it but I stopped decoying those final four games. I couldn't know if they would make a rule this year that a pitcher could not touch his head, or something. I had so long made a habit of those finger moves, I wanted to begin to break the habit, just in case. It didn't seem to hurt my pitching, and I may have given a few clubs something to think about for the future.

I've moved back home again, living in North Carolina, the father of four fine children, the husband of an outstanding wife. I've come back in excellent health to three tobacco plantations, an interest in an insurance business and several duplex apartment buildings. I'm earning $100,000 a year and I've got some good baseball seasons ahead of me yet. Not bad, I guess, for a barefoot boy who didn't know electricity or indoor plumbing until he went to Williamston High. I want to thank everybody who made it possible: me and the spitter.

Postscript

It isn't really any concern of mine any more, except as an interested observer, but I think the Major League Rules Committee made a big mistake when they changed the spitter-greaser rule in December, 1973. I was all for a change—but not the one they made. Instead of legalizing the slick pitch—which I advocate—the Rules Committee decided that, from now on, an umpire can just look at a pitch, watch the way it reacts and, on that basis alone, call it a spitter or a greaser or a plain illegal delivery.

The first time the umpire thinks he sees a spitter, he's supposed to call the pitch a ball, warn the pitcher not to do it again and tell the fans over the public-address system that the pitcher just did something nasty and unclean. The second time the umpire thinks he sees the spitter, he's supposed to kick the pitcher out of the game and make him subject to a fine.

Up until this rule change, the umpires actually had to find a foreign substance on the ball. Now they don't have to find anything. All they've got to do is *think* something, think they see a pitch acting in a funny way that could not have been produced by natural causes.

I think this new rule puts a terrible burden on the umpires. Even the best umpires have trouble sometimes telling the difference between a ball and a strike, so my question is: How are they supposed to tell the difference between a fork ball and a spitter, a knuckler and a greaser, a slider and a sweat ball?

Managers like Billy Martin and Ralph Houk have never hesitated to tell umpires what they ought to *see*. Now they're certainly going to tell them what they ought to *think*. The hollering and the crying is going to be terrible. There won't be any time left to play ball.

Like I say, it isn't going to affect me personally, unless the Rules Committee comes out and prohibits sweat—then I'll have to keep a bottle of talcum powder on the mound —but I think the new spitter rule is ridiculous. Every year, the odds mount against the pitcher: the mound gets lower, the ball gets livelier, the strike zone shrinks, the designated hitter comes in. Eventually, I suppose, they'll just use slow-pitch pitching machines, and then a tabulator to count up all the home runs.

I'm kind of sorry I didn't get to pitch in the old days, when anything went, but I am glad at least I've been able to do my pitching during a time when a little ingenuity didn't hurt a man any.

Of course, now, maybe when I'm finished playing ball, I could get a job as consultant, or supervisor, for the umpires. I could spend the rest of my life serving up spitters—just so the umpires could learn what it is they're expected to think they see.